STONE TEMPLE PILOTS

CORE

AMSCO PUBLICATIONS
New York • London • Sydney

Special Thanks to Eric Greenspan, Barrie Edwards, Roland Ottewell, and Dan Earley

Management: Steve Stewart

Cover photography: Katrina Dickson
Interior photography: Lisa Johnson and Atlantic Records
Art director: Kevin Hosmann
Guitar transcriptions: Jeff Catania, Chris Celano, Sim Flick, Hemme Luttjeboer, and Dale Turner
Music engraving: Chelsea Music Engraving

Order No. AM 91464
US International Standard Book Number: 0.8256.1371.X
UK International Standard Book Number: 0.7119.3701.X

Exclusive Distributors:
Music Sales Corporation
225 Park Avenue South, New York, NY 10003 USA
Music Sales Limited
8/9 Frith Street, London W1U 5TZ England
Music Sales Pty. Limited
120 Rothschild Street, Rosebery, Sydney, NSW 2018, Australia

Printed in the United States of America by
Vicks Lithograph and Printing Corporation

CONTENTS

LEGEND OF MUSIC SYMBOLS

DEAD & BLOATED

WORDS AND MUSIC BY SCOTT WEILAND, DEAN DELEO, ROBERT DELEO AND ERIC KRETZ

Slow half-time feel

No chord

I am smell-in' like the rose that some - bo - dy gave me on my birth - day death-bed.

I am smell-in' like the rose that some - bo - dy gave me 'cause I'm dead and bloat - ed.

guitar 1 (with distortion)

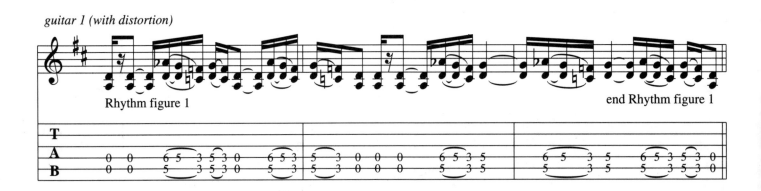

Rhythm figure 1   end Rhythm figure 1

with Rhythm figure 1 (2 times)

N.C. (D5)

1.-3. I am smell-in' like the rose that some- bo - dy gave me on my birth-day death-bed.

to Coda ⊕

1.,3. I am smell-in' like the rose that some - bo - dy gave me 'cause I'm dead and bloat-ed.⎫
(2. only) I am tram-pled un-der sole of an - oth - er man's shoes, guess I walked too soft - ly.⎭

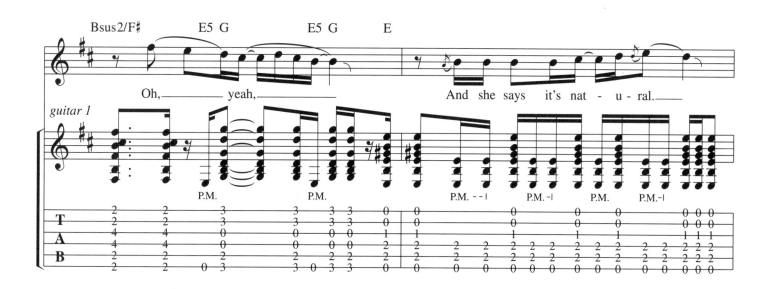

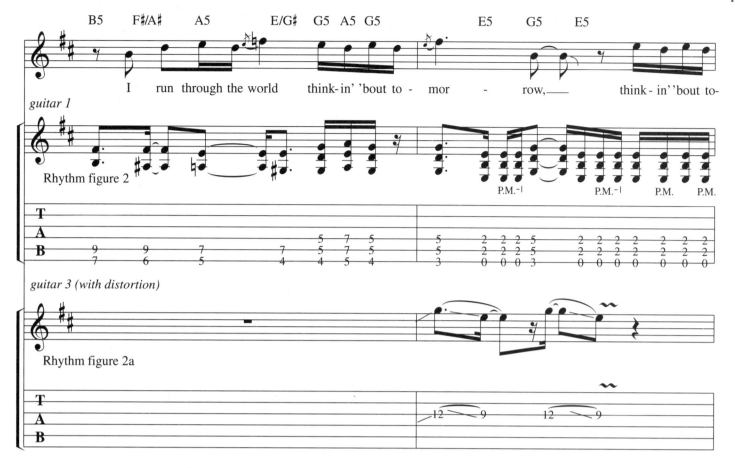

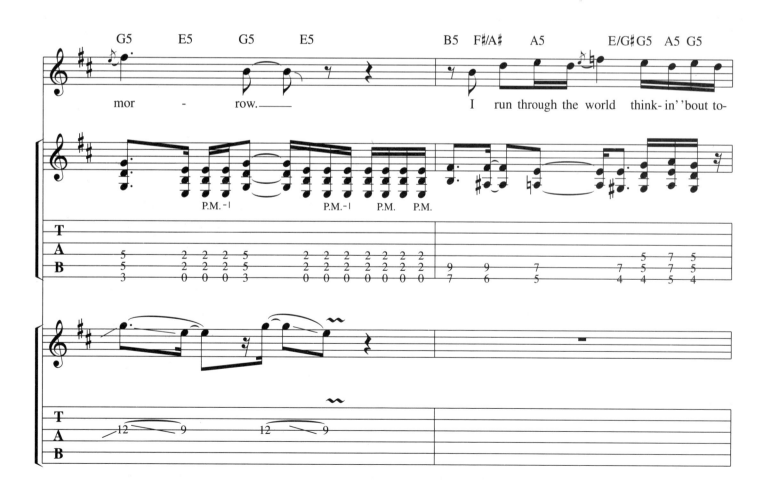

12

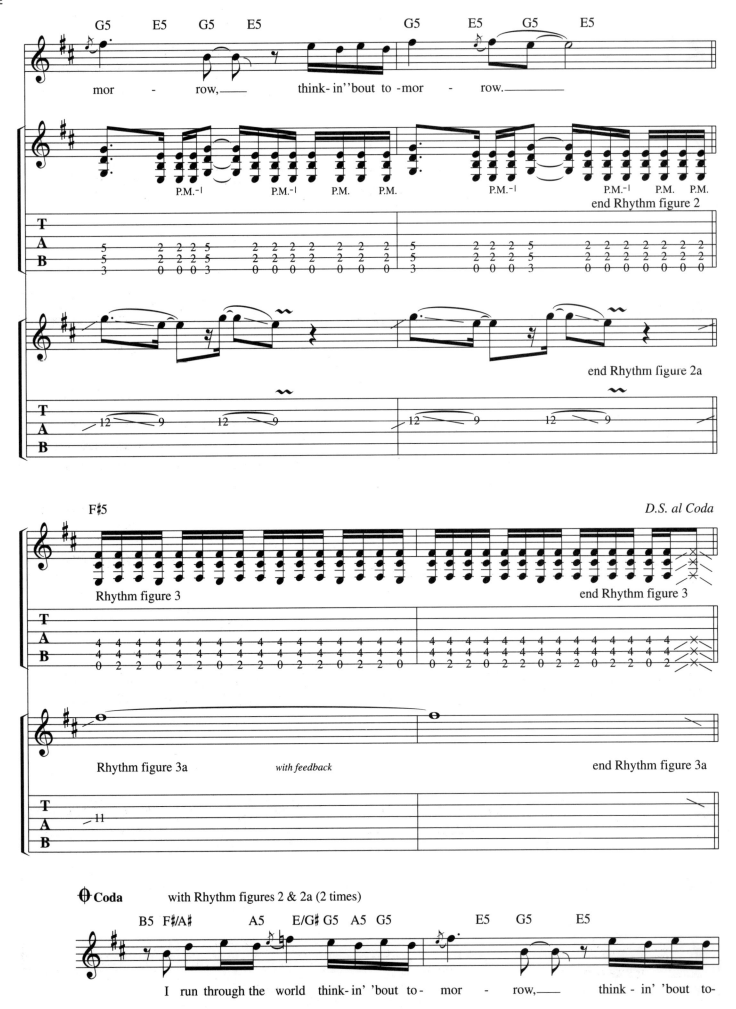

13

SEX TYPE THING

WORDS AND MUSIC BY SCOTT WEILAND, DEAN DELEO, ROBERT DELEO AND ERIC KRETZ

*Fret positions are approximate. Move gradually toward nut from 3rd fret

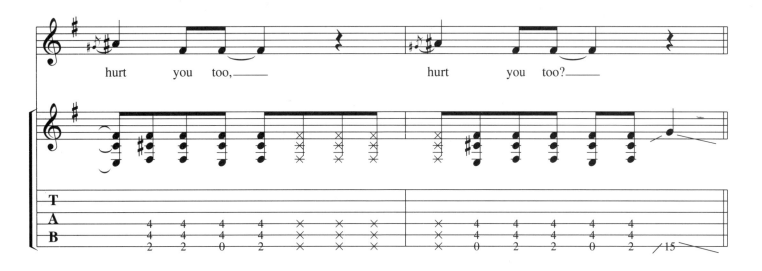

hurt   you   too,____   hurt   you   too?____

with Rhythm figures 1 & 1a (2 times)

E5   E(♭5)   E A5   E5 G6   Asus2 G6 E5   E(♭5) E5   A5   E5 G5   Asus2 G6 E5

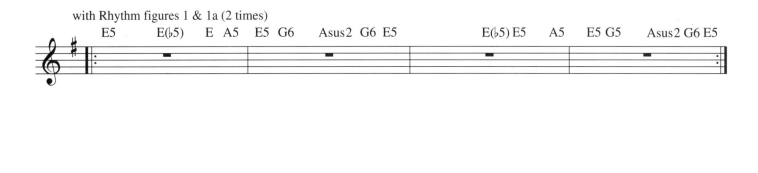

F♯5

I ain't,   I ain't,   I ain't____ a-buy-in' in-to your   a - pa-thy.____

guitar 1

Rhythm figure 2

guitar 2

Rhythm figure 2a

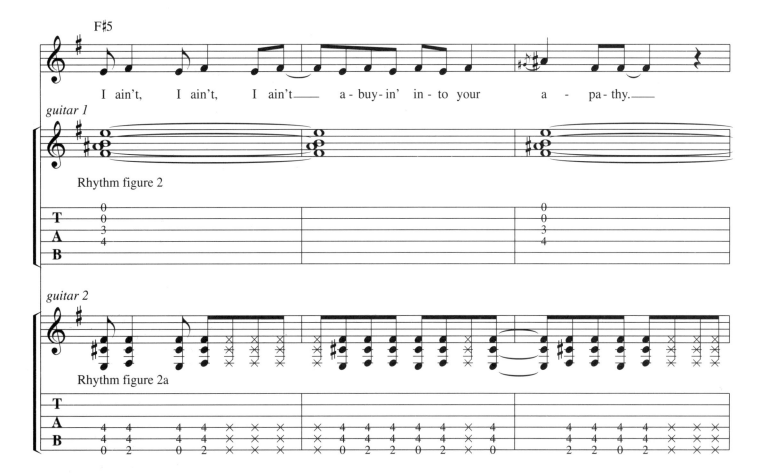

I'm gon-na learn ya my phil - o - soph- y.____ You wan- na know a- bout a-

*Move gradually toward nut from 3rd fret

B5

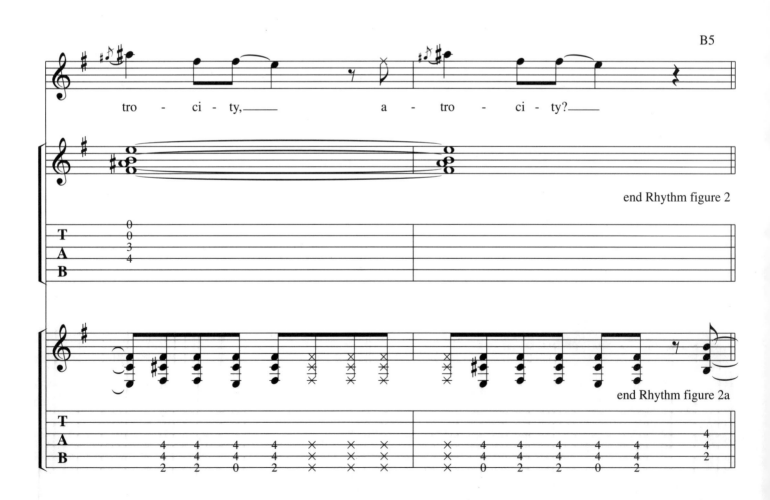

tro - ci - ty,____ a - tro - ci - ty?____

end Rhythm figure 2

end Rhythm figure 2a

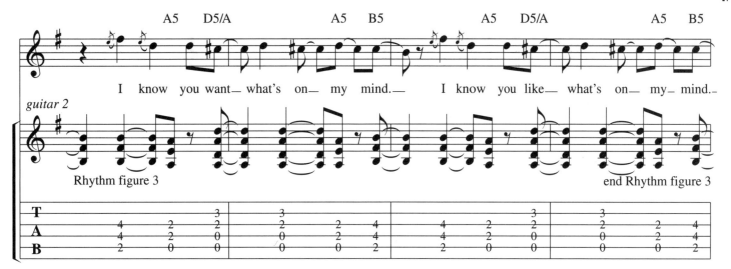

guitar 2

Rhythm figure 3   end Rhythm figure 3

I know you want— what's on— my mind.— I know you like— what's on— my— mind.—

with Rhythm figure 3

— I know it eats— you up— in - side. I know you know,— you know, you know.

with Rhythm figures 1 & 1a (2 times)

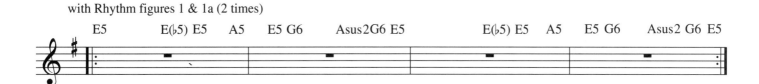

with Rhythm figures 2 & 2a

I am a man, a man,— I'll give ya some-thin' that ya won't— for-get.—

I said ya should-n't have—— worn that dress.——

I said ya should-n't have— worn that dress,— worn that dress.—

*Fret positions are approximate. Move gradually toward nut from 3rd fret

*Fret positions are approximate. Move gradually from 2nd to 3rd fret

with Rhythm figure 3 (4 times)

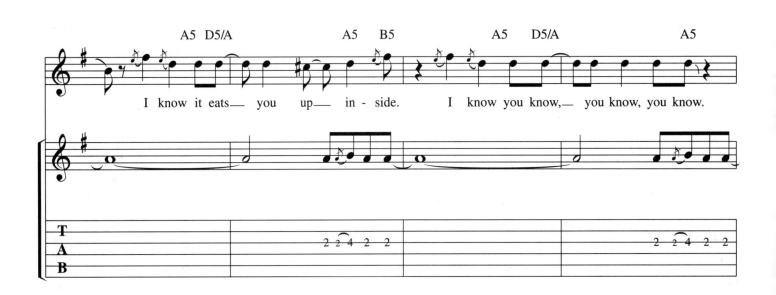

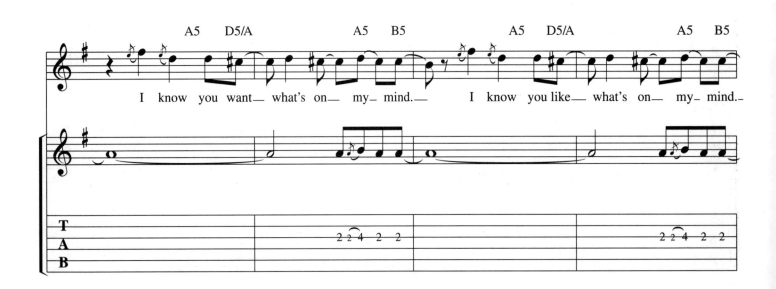

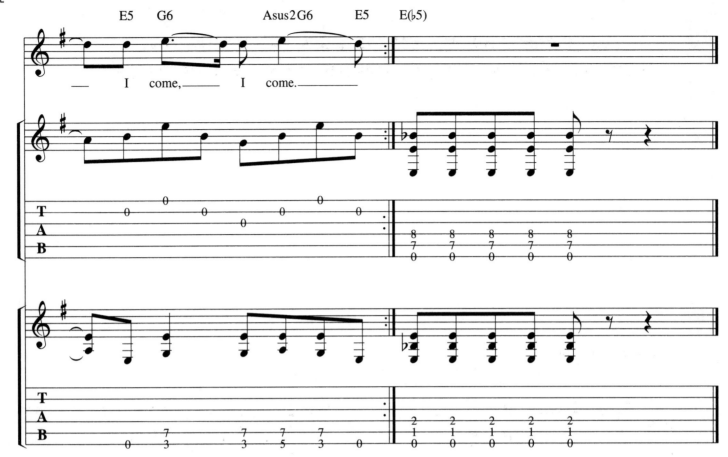

I come,—— I come.——

WICKED GARDEN

WORDS AND MUSIC BY SCOTT WEILAND, DEAN DELEO, ROBERT DELEO AND ERIC KRETZ

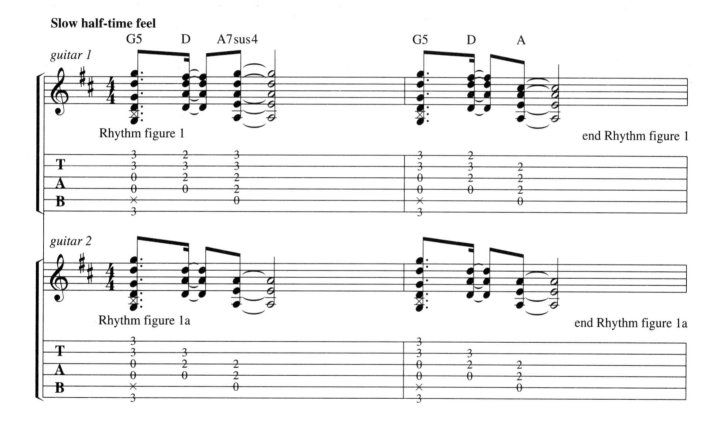

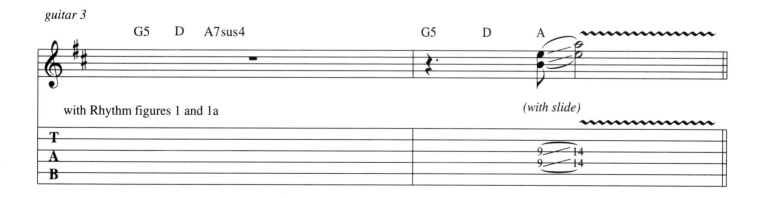

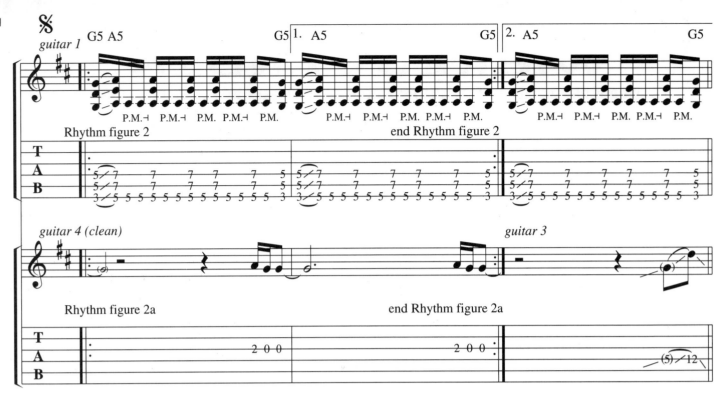

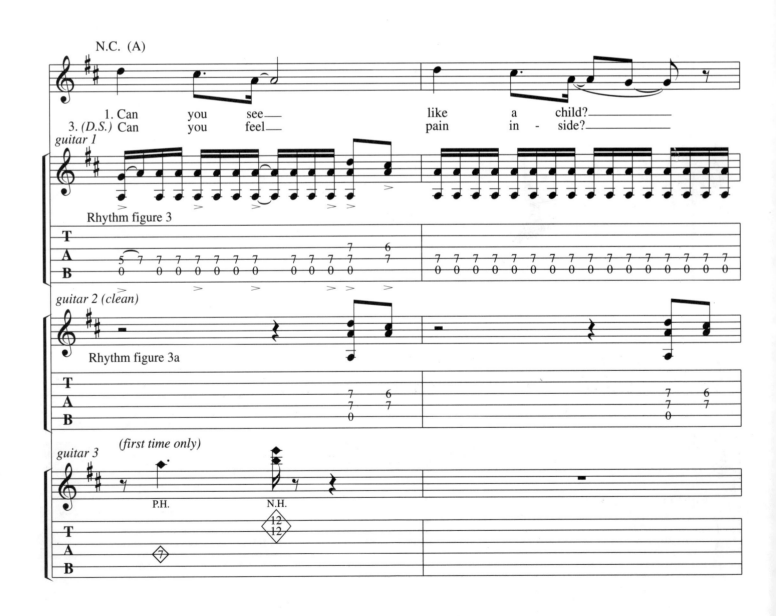

A5 G5

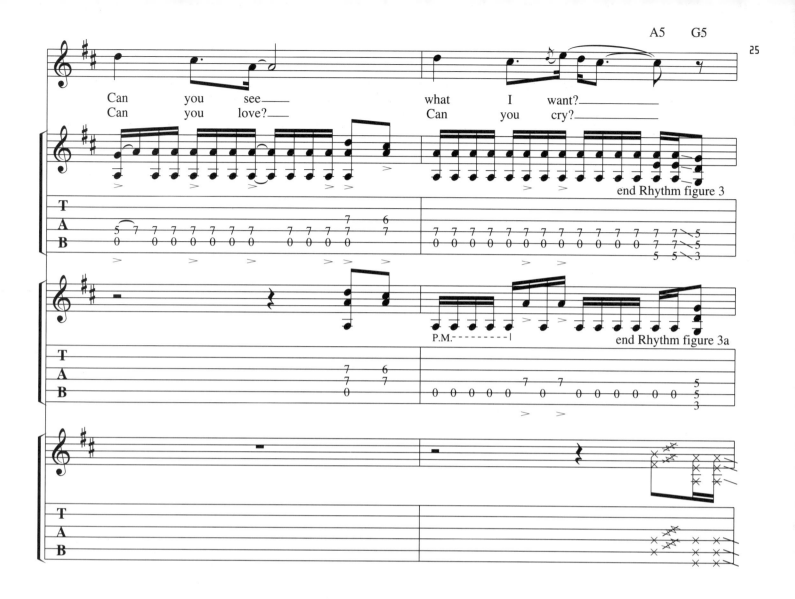

Can you see——   what I want?——
Can you love?——

Can I you cry?——

end Rhythm figure 3

P.M.- - - - - - - - -| end Rhythm figure 3a

with Rhythm figures 2 & 2a

A5   G5 A5   G5

I wan - na run through your wick - ed gar - den. Heard that's the place to find— you.—

to Coda ⊕

A5   G5 A5   G5

'Cause I'm a - live,— so— a - live,— now. I know the dark - ness blinds— you.

guitar 3

W.B.- - - - - - - - - -|

with Rhythm figures 3 & 3a

N.C. (A)   A5 G5

2. Can you see— with-out eyes?___ Can you speak— with-out lies?___

with Rhythm figures 2 & 2a

A5   G5   A5   G5

I wan-na drink—from your nak-ed foun-tain.— I can drown— your sor - rows.—

A5   G5   A5   F♯5

I'm gon-na burn,— burn you to life,— now, Out of the chains that bind— you.

guitars 1 & 2

P.M.⌐ P.M.⌐ P.M. P.M.⌐ P.M.   P.M.⌐   P.M.⌐   P.M. P.M.⌐ P.M.

D5   B5   F♯5

Can   you   see—   just   like   a   child?

Rhythm figure 4   end Rhythm figure 4

with Rhythm figure 4 (2 times)

D5   B5   F♯5   D5   B5   F♯5

Can   you   see—   just what   I want?—   Can I bring—   you back   to   life?

D.S. al Coda

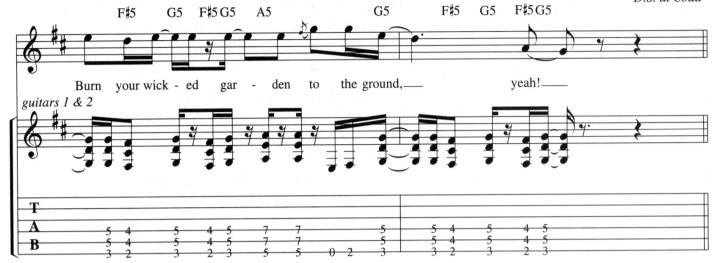

Burn your wick - ed gar - den to the ground,___ yeah!___

guitars 1 & 2

Coda   with Rhythm figure 4 (3 times)

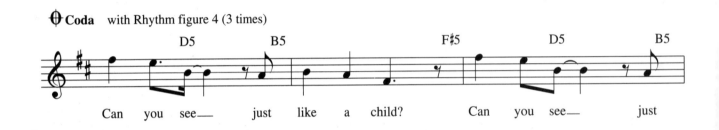

Can you see___ just like a child? Can you see___ just

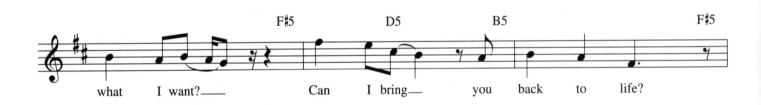

what I want?___ Can I bring___ you back to life?

Are you still___ a - live?___

with Rhythm figure 5 (3 times)

Burn, burn,— burn._____ Burn— your— wick - ed
*(Burn, burn, burn, burn.)*_____

gar - den down. Burn,_____ burn,— burn._____
*(Burn, burn, burn, burn.)*_____

Burn your wick - ed gar - den to the ground,_____ yeah!

guitars 1 & 2

with Rhythm figures 1 and 1a (2 times)
guitar 3

(with slide)

SIN

WORDS AND MUSIC BY SCOTT WEILAND, DEAN DELEO, ROBERT DELEO AND ERIC KRETZ

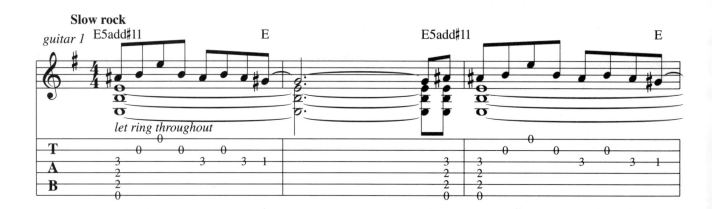

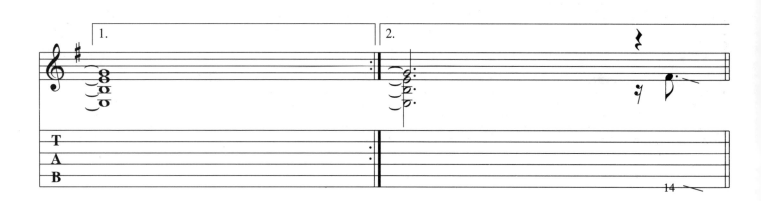

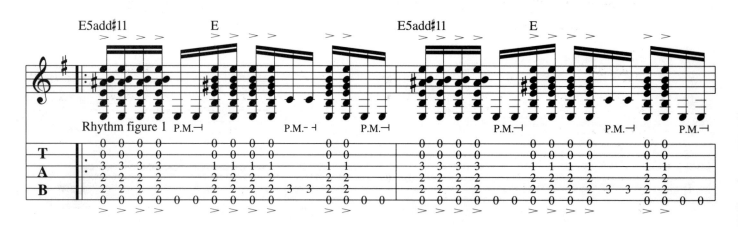

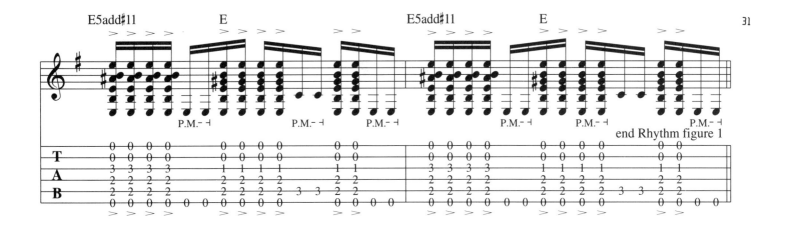

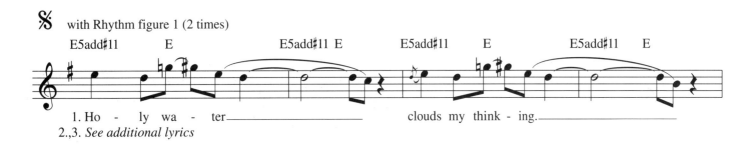

1. Ho - ly wa - ter_____ clouds my think - ing._____

2.,3. *See additional lyrics*

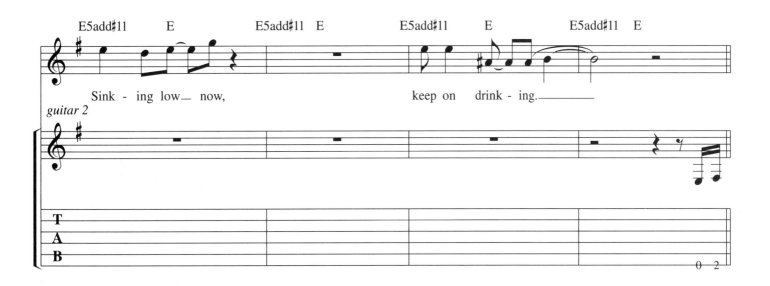

Sink - ing low— now, keep on drink - ing._____

guitar 2

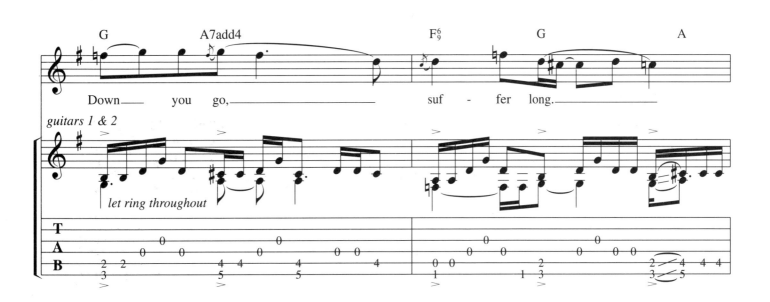

Down—— you go,————————— suf - fer long.——

guitars 1 & 2

let ring throughout

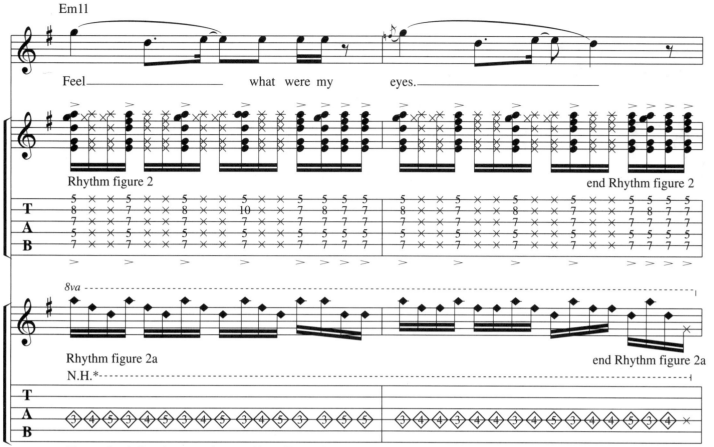

Em11

Feel_____ what were my eyes._____

Rhythm figure 2

end Rhythm figure 2

8va- -

Rhythm figure 2a

end Rhythm figure 2a

N.H.*- -|

*Fret numbers indicated are approximate positions of harmonics

with Rhythm figures 2 & 2a *simile* (3 times)

Em11

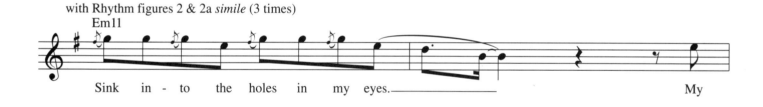

Sink in - to the holes in my eyes._____ My

sins_____ have made me_____ blind._____

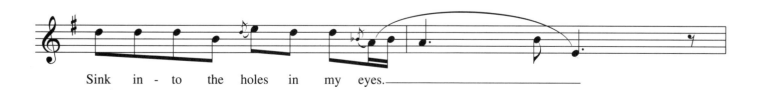

Sink in - to the holes in my eyes._____

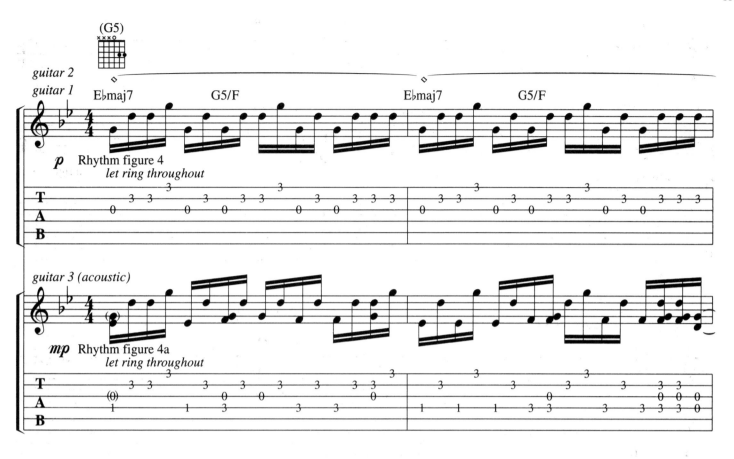

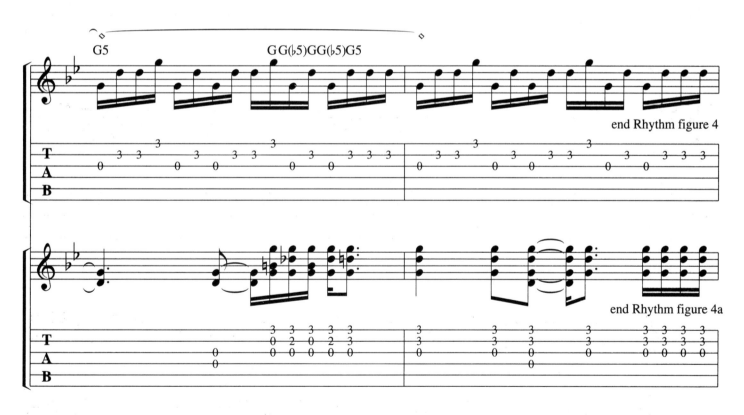

with Rhythm figures 4 & 4a *simile* (2 times) (guitars 1 & 3)

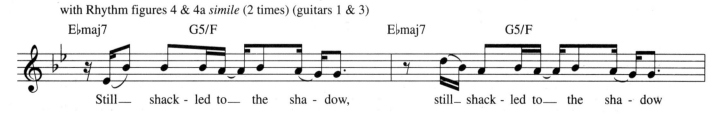

Still— shack - led to— the sha - dow,　　still— shack - led to— the sha - dow

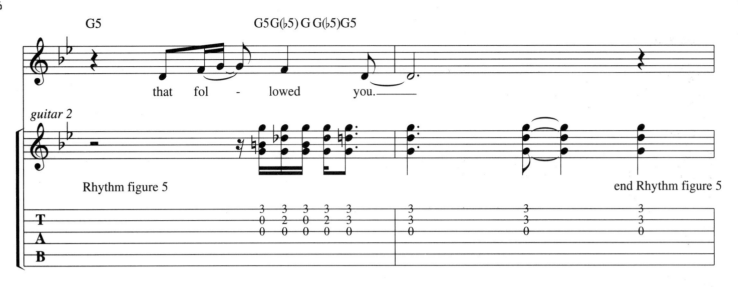

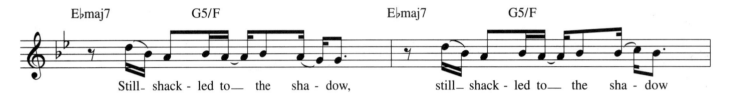

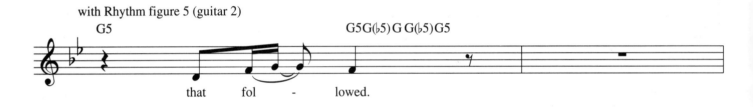

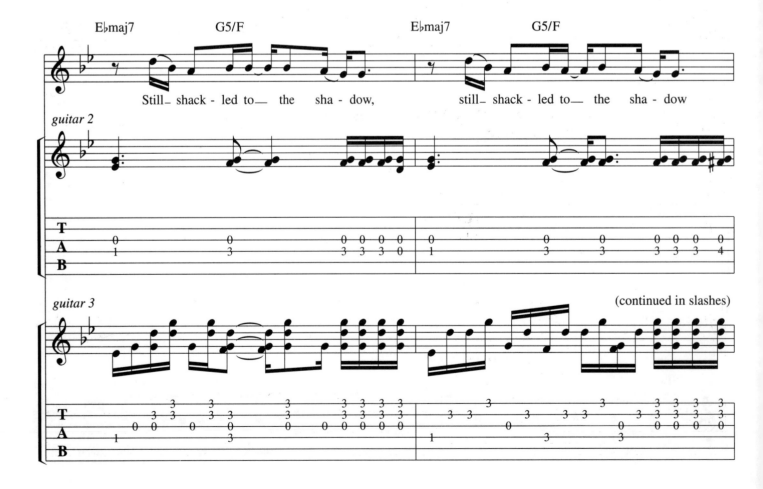

with Rhythm figure 3

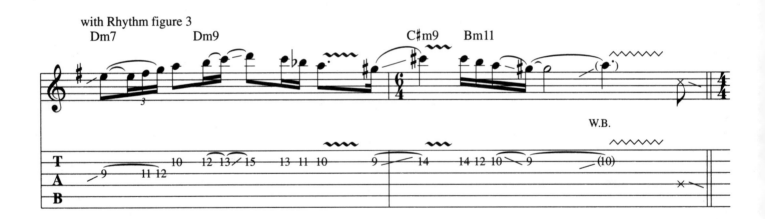

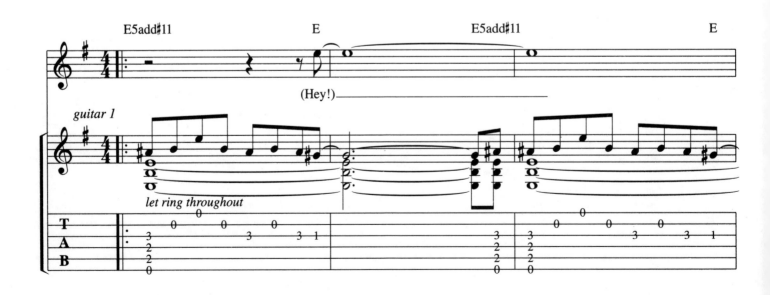

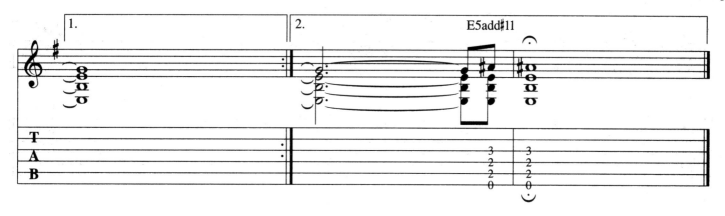

Additional lyrics

2. You control me, soul you stole, mine.
   Wishful thinking, six feet under.
3. Dead by dreaming, sleep you steal, mine.
   Pools of cold sweat, hatred burns me.

NO MEMORY

WORDS AND MUSIC BY SCOTT WEILAND, DEAN DELEO, ROBERT DELEO AND ERIC KRETZ

Moderately slow

guitar 1 (acoustic)   *fade in*

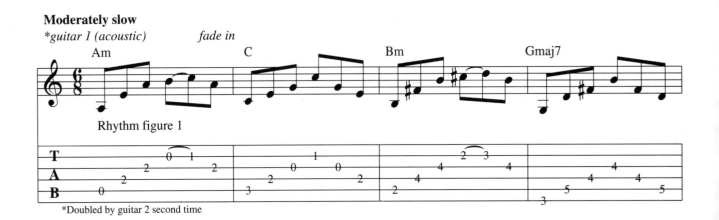

Rhythm figure 1

*Doubled by guitar 2 second time

end Rhythm figure 1

with Rhythm figure 1 (guitar 2)

guitar 1

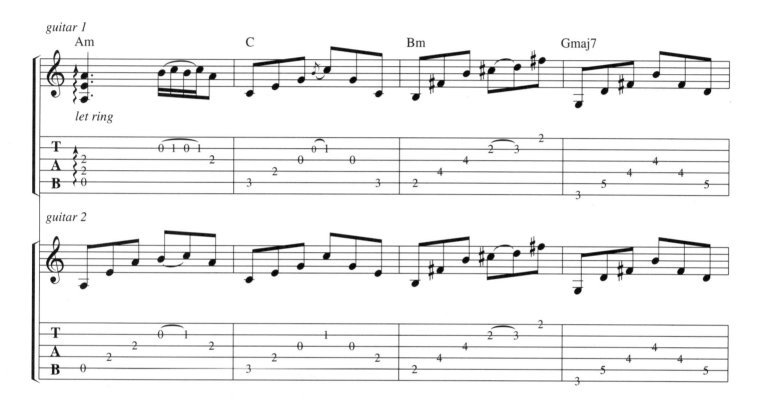

with Rhythm figure 1
guitar 1

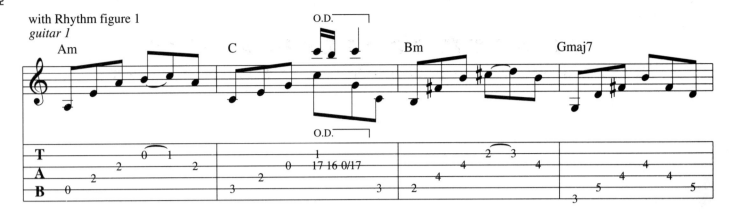

(segue to "Sin")

NAKED SUNDAY

WORDS AND MUSIC BY SCOTT WEILAND, DEAN DELEO, ROBERT DELEO AND ERIC KRETZ

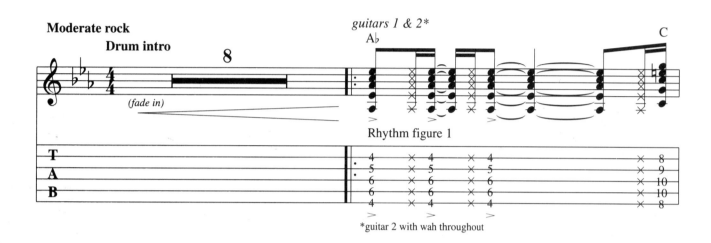

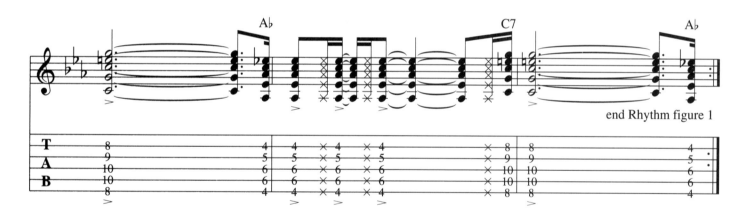

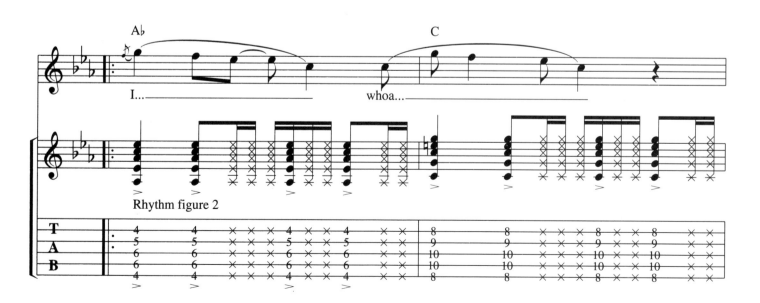

with Rhythm figures 1 and 3

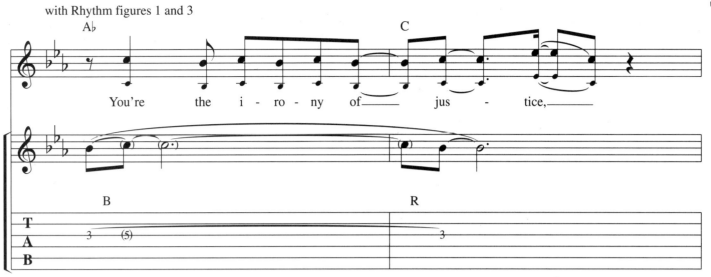

You're the i - ro - ny of____ jus - tice,____

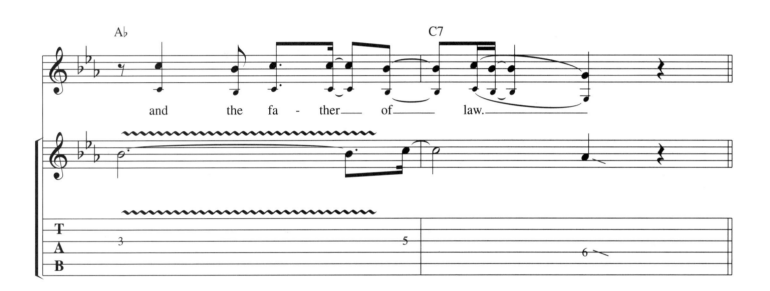

and the fa - ther____ of____ law.____

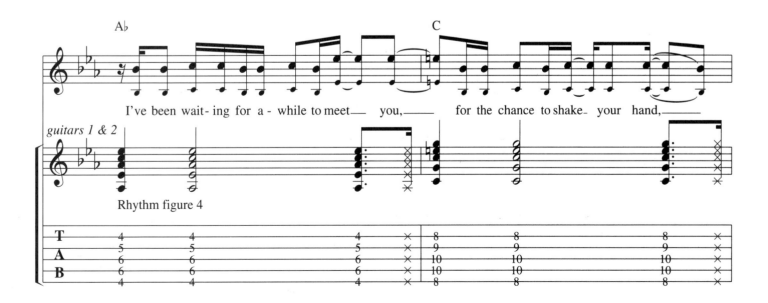

I've been wait- ing for a - while to meet____ you,____ for the chance to shake_ your hand,____

guitars 1 & 2

Rhythm figure 4

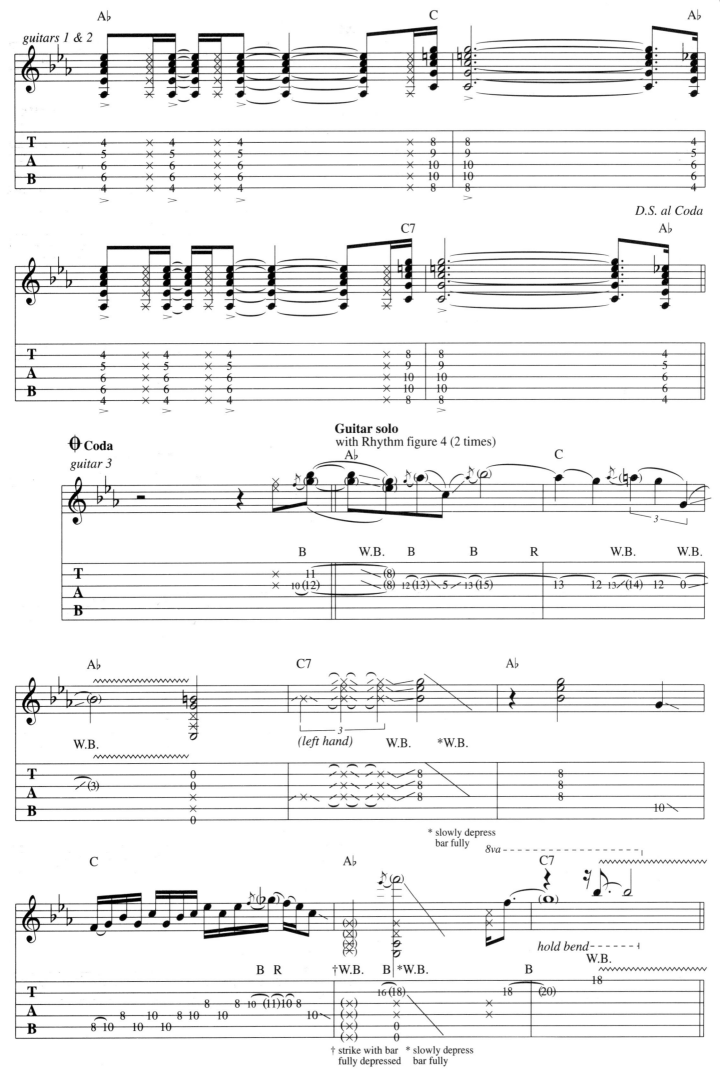

with Rhythm figure 1 (2 times)

(Quasi spoken:) An — eye — for an eye, — and a tooth — for a

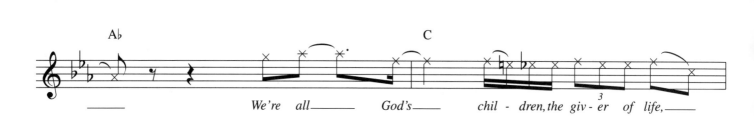

tooth, — turn — the — oth - er — cheek a - side. —

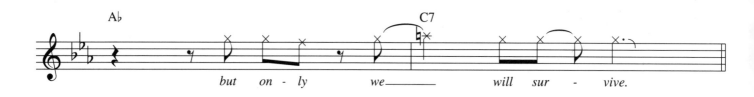

— We're all — God's — chil - dren, the giv - er of life, —

but on - ly we — will sur - vive.

I... whoa...

I... yeah.

I... whoa...

I... yeah.

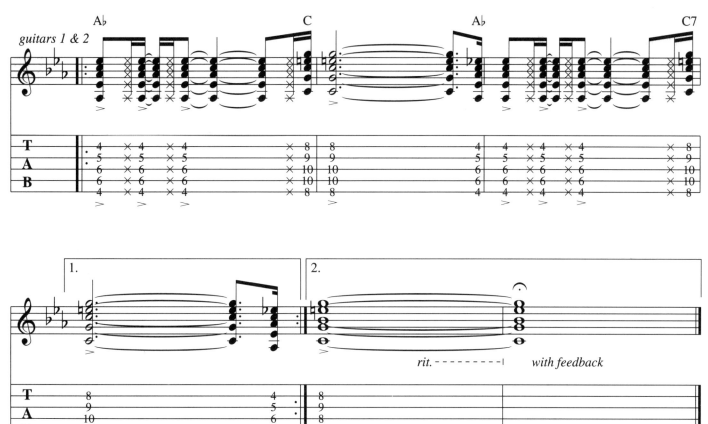

Additional lyrics

2. You're the champion of sorrow
   You're the love and the pain
   You're the fighter of evil,
   Yet you're one and the same.

PLUSH

WORDS AND MUSIC BY SCOTT WEILAND, DEAN DELEO, ROBERT DELEO AND ERIC KRETZ

Moderately slow

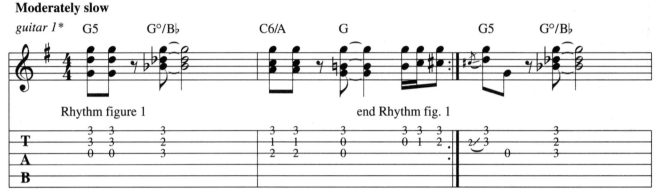

*Two guitars arranged for one

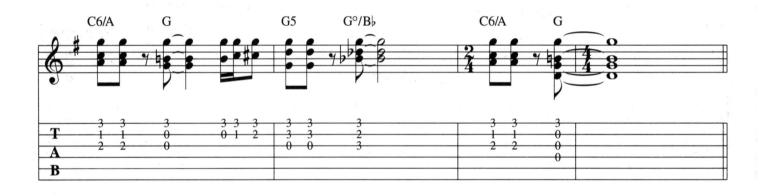

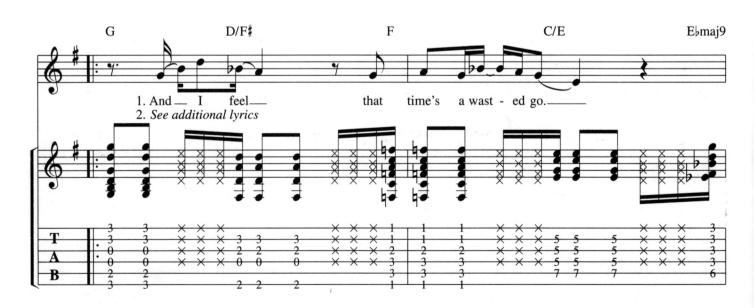

1. And — I feel— that time's a wast - ed go.—
2. *See additional lyrics*

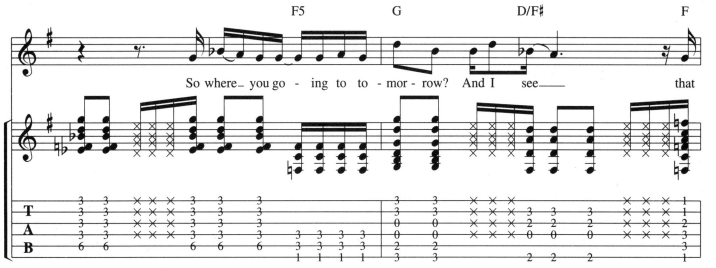

So where_ you go - ing to to - mor - row? And I see_____ that

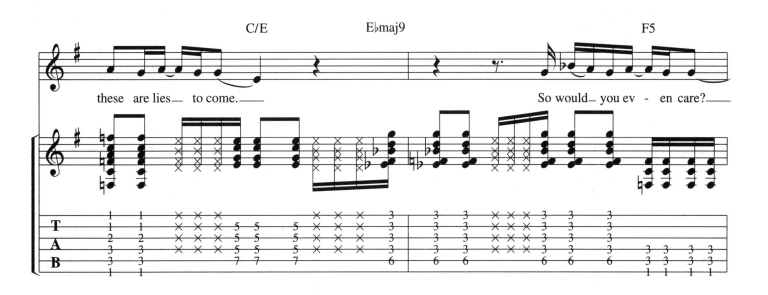

these are lies_ to come._____ So would_ you ev - en care?_____

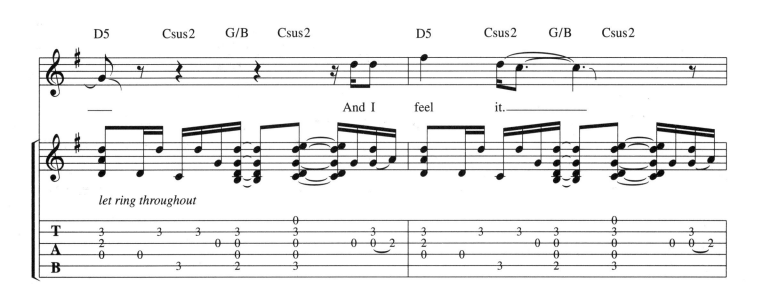

And I feel it._____

let ring throughout

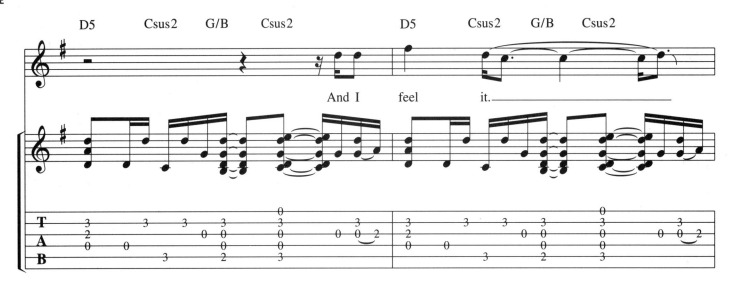

And I feel it._____

Where ya go - ing for to - mor - row?_____

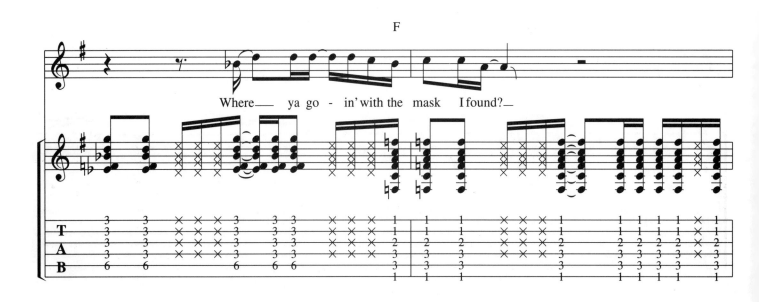

Where___ ya go - in' with the mask I found?___

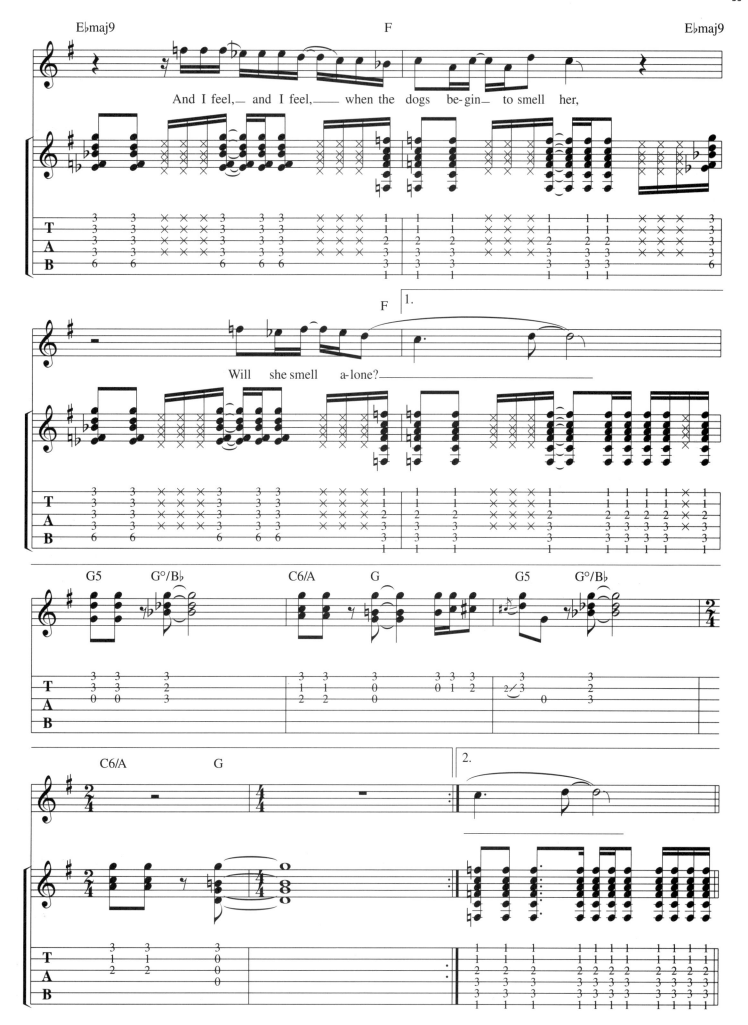

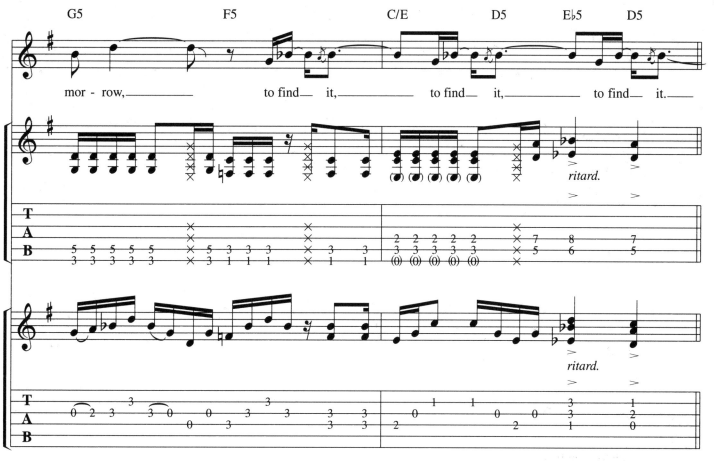

mor - row,_____ to find__ it,_____ to find__ it,_____ to find__ it._____

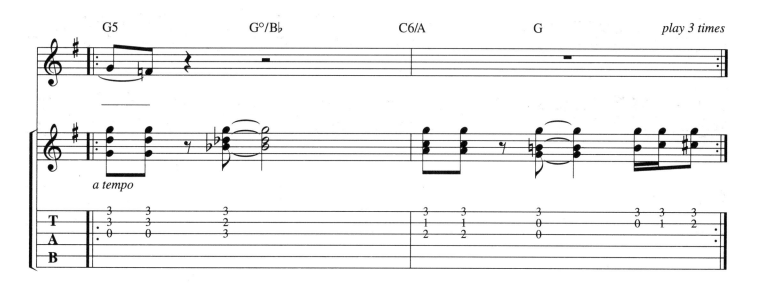

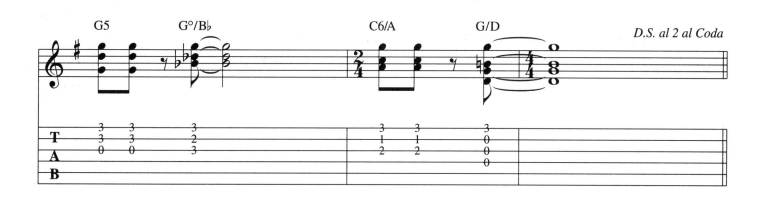

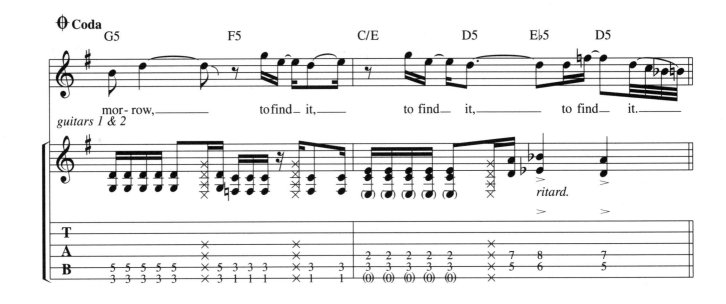

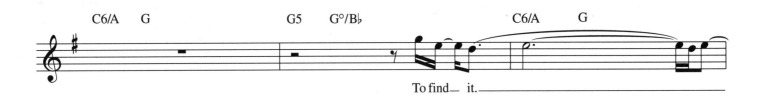

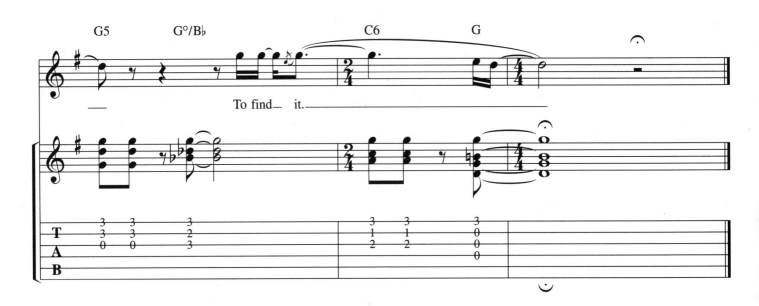

Additional lyrics

2. And I feel, so much depends upon the weather.
So is it raining in your bedroom?
And I see, that these are the eyes of disarray.
Would you even care?

And I feel it.
And she feels it.

CREEP

WORDS AND MUSIC BY SCOTT WEILAND, DEAN DELEO, ROBERT DELEO AND ERIC KRETZ

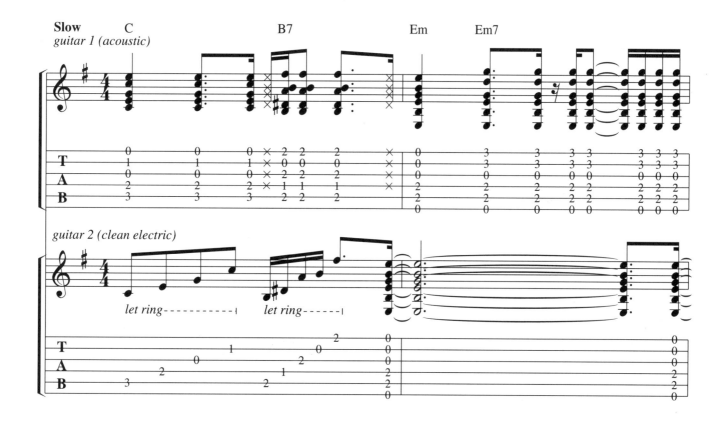

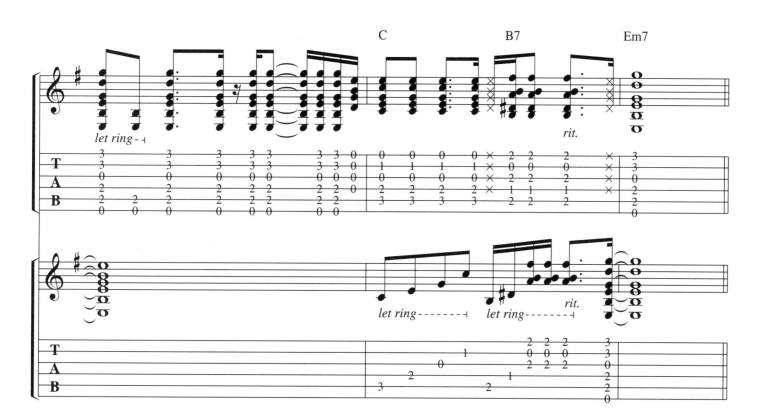

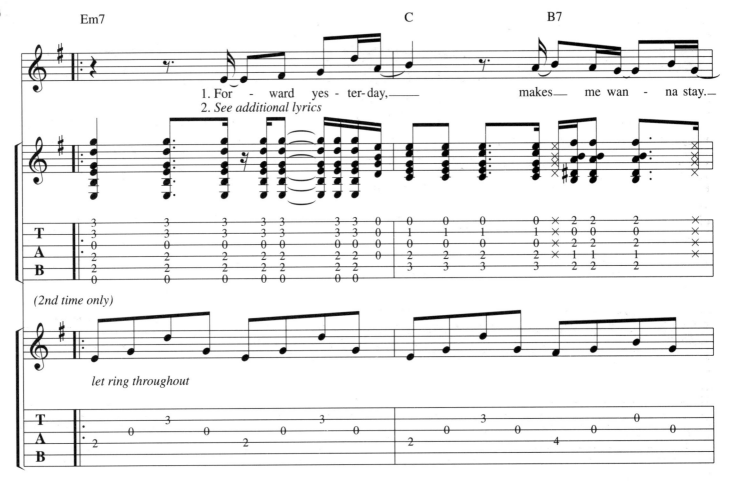

1. For - ward yes - ter- day,_____ makes_ me wan - na stay._
2. *See additional lyrics*

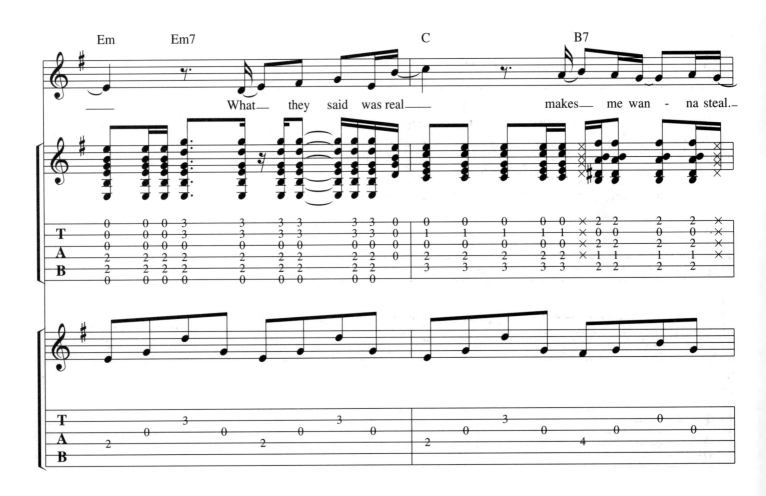

What_ they said was real_____ makes_ me wan - na steal._

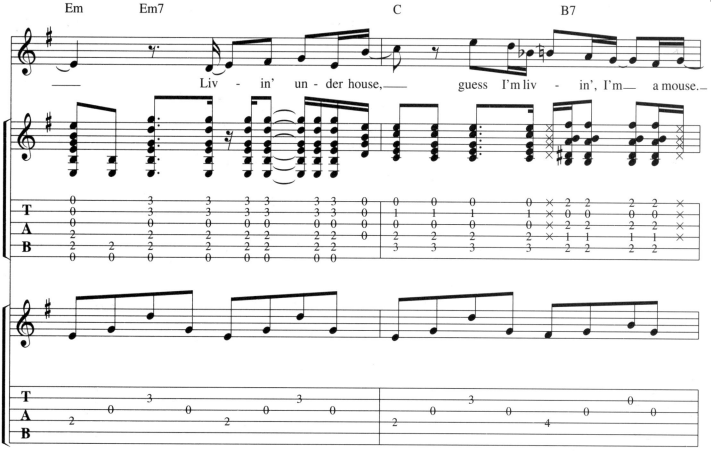

Liv - in' un - der house,____ guess I'm liv - in', I'm____ a mouse.____

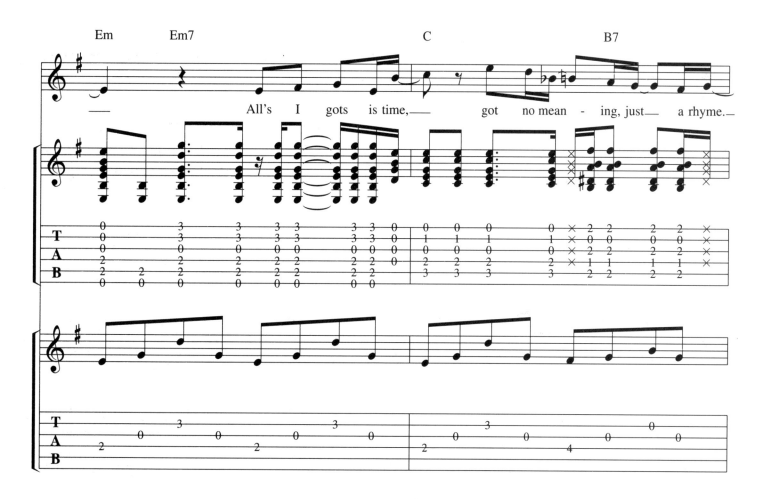

All's I gots is time,____ got no mean - ing, just____ a rhyme.____

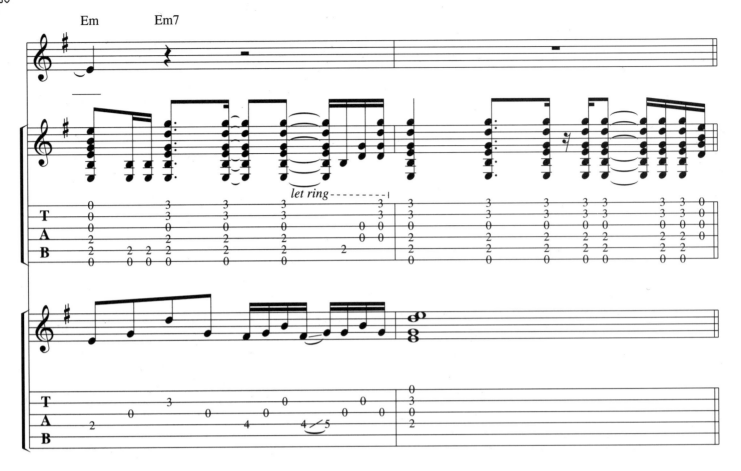

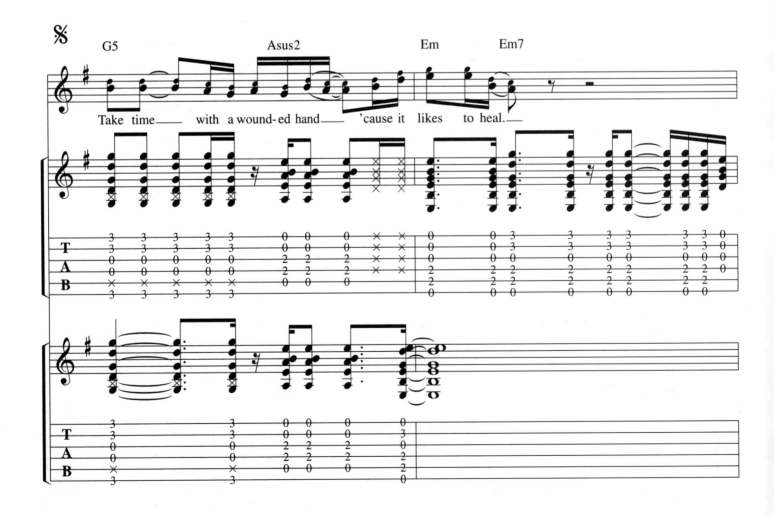

Take time___ with a wound-ed hand___ 'cause it likes to heal.___

(cue notes 2nd and 3rd times only)

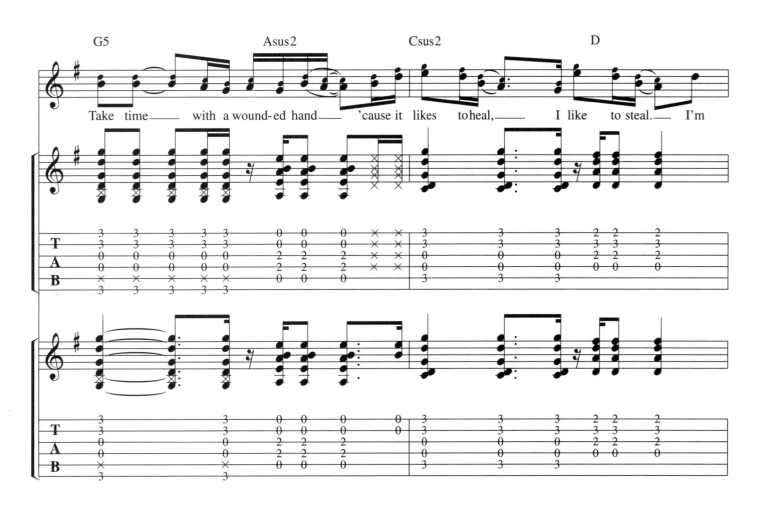

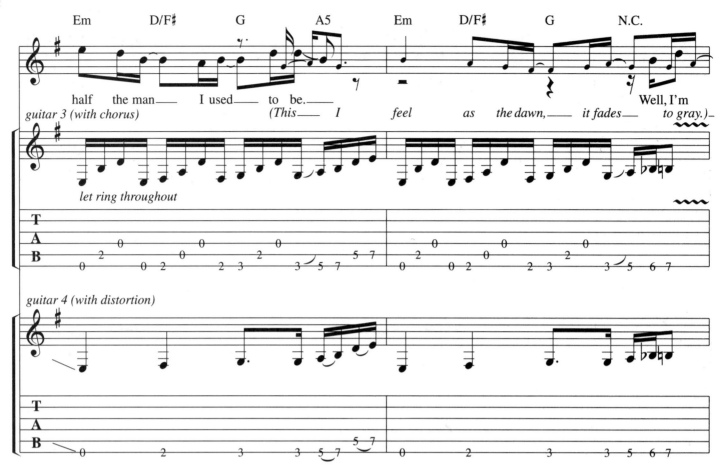

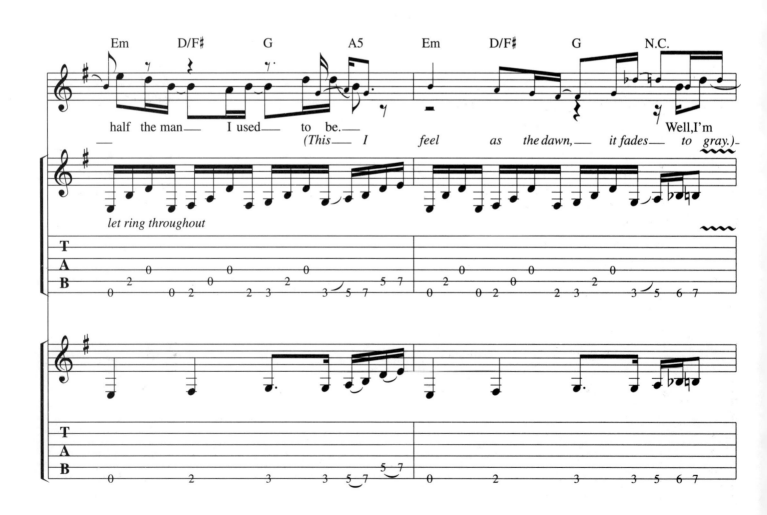

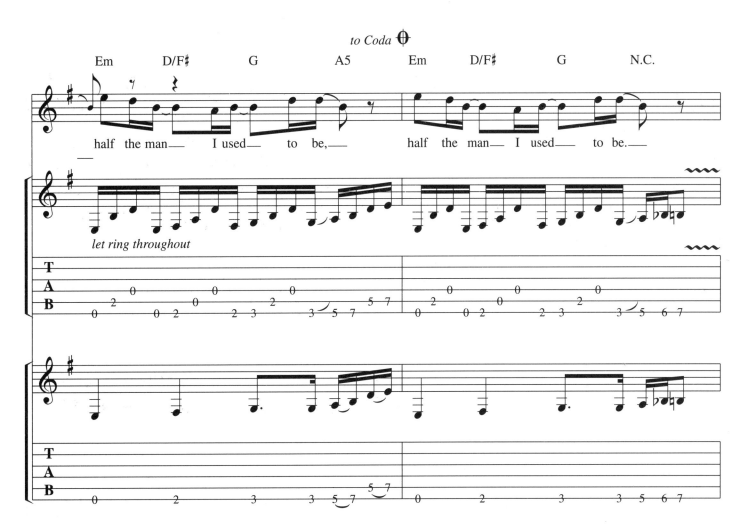

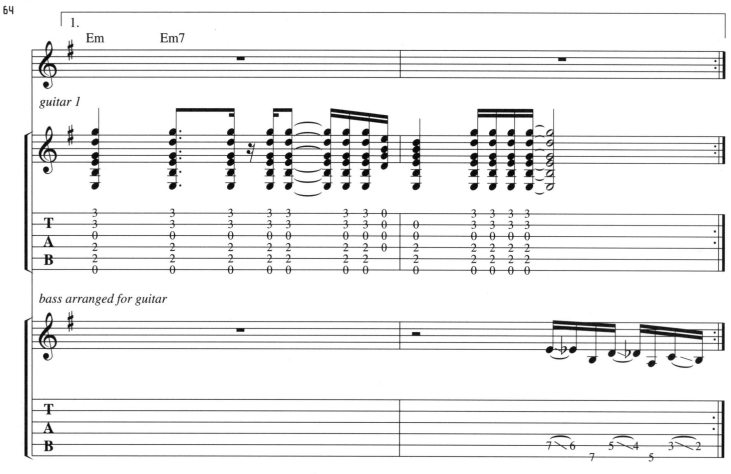

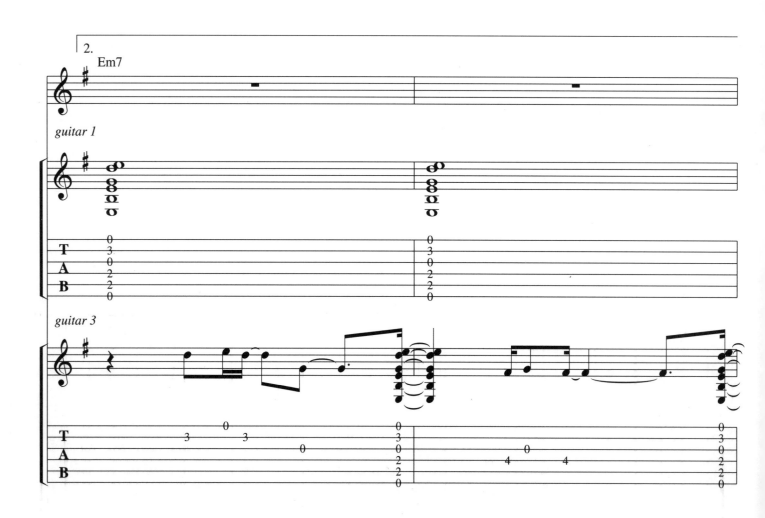

Additional lyrics

2. Feelin' uninspired, think I'll start a fire.
   Everybody run, Bobby's got a gun.
   Think you're kinda neat, then she tells me I'm a creep.
   Friends don't mean a thing, guess I'll leave it up to me.

PIECE OF PIE

WORDS AND MUSIC BY SCOTT WEILAND, DEAN DELEO, ROBERT DELEO AND ERIC KRETZ

Tune down
½ step:
① E♭ ④ D♭
② B♭ ⑤ A♭
③ G♭ ⑥ E♭

Moderately slow

N.C. (E5)
guitars 1 & 2 (with distortion)

Yeah.

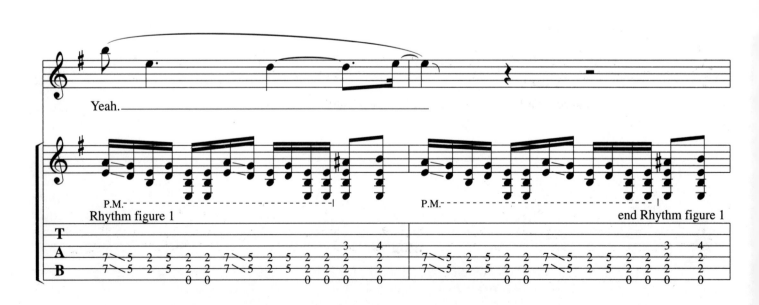

Rhythm figure 1

end Rhythm figure 1

Yeah.

2nd time substitute Rhythm figure 1 in 1st 4 bars

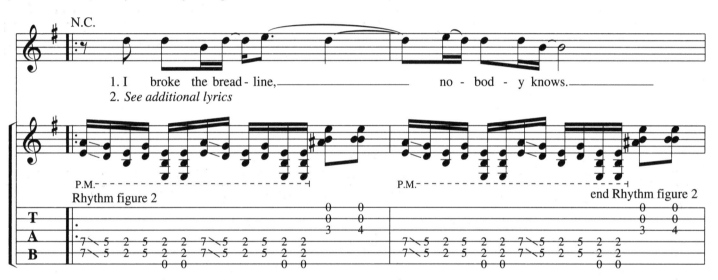

1. I broke the bread - line,_____ no - bod - y knows._____
2. *See additional lyrics*

Rhythm figure 2

end Rhythm figure 2

with Rhythm figure 2 (2 times)

I walked the front__ line,_____ still got far to go.__

I__ mixed the wa - ter,_____ I__ drank the wa - ter._____

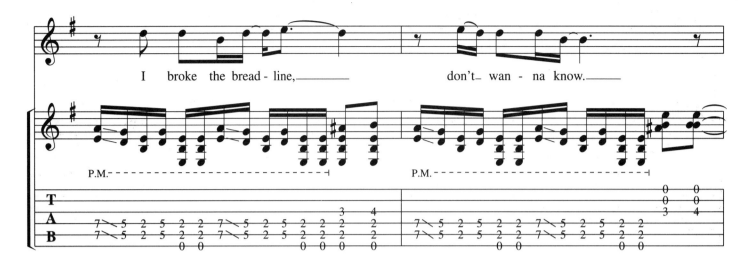

I broke the bread - line,_____ don't_ wan - na know._____

Yeah,____ yeah,____ *(2nd time):* Yeah,____ It's

𝄋 Chorus

N.C.   (D5)(E5)   N.C.   (D5) (A/C♯)   N.C.   (D5)(E5)   N.C.   (D5)(E5)

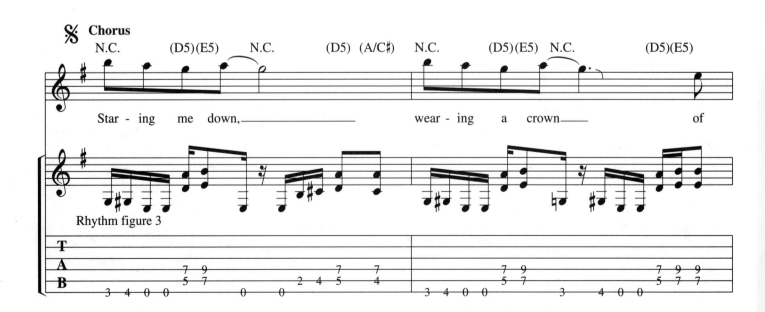

Star - ing me down,_____ wear - ing a crown_____ of

Rhythm figure 3

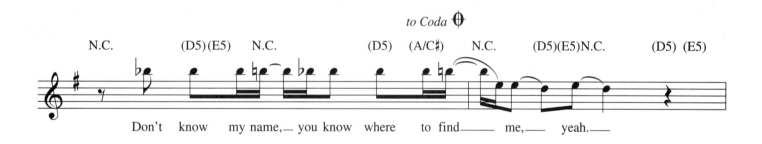

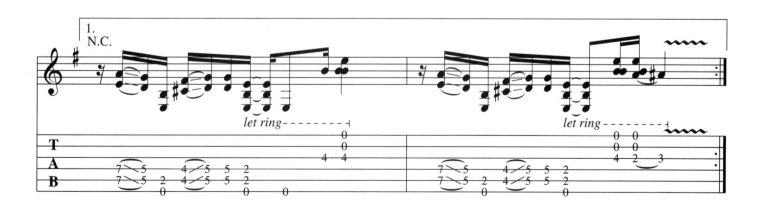

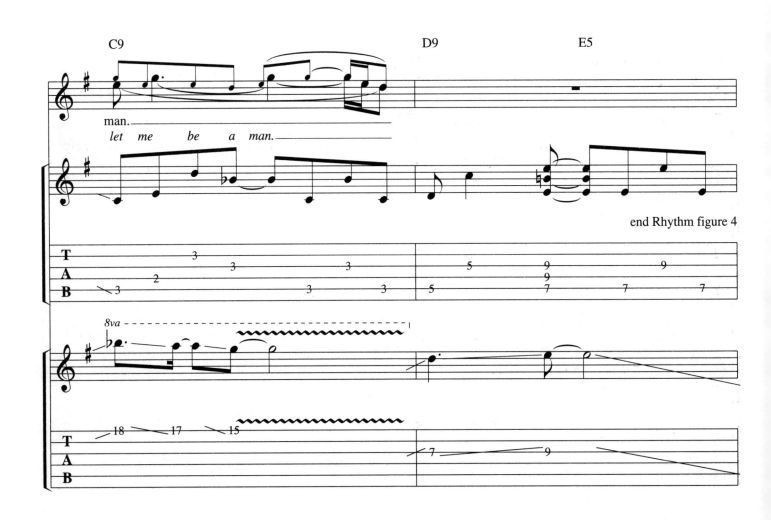

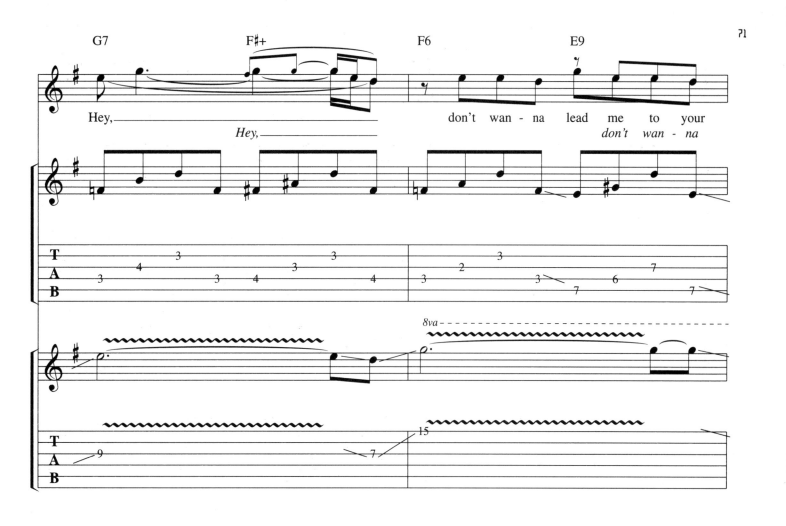

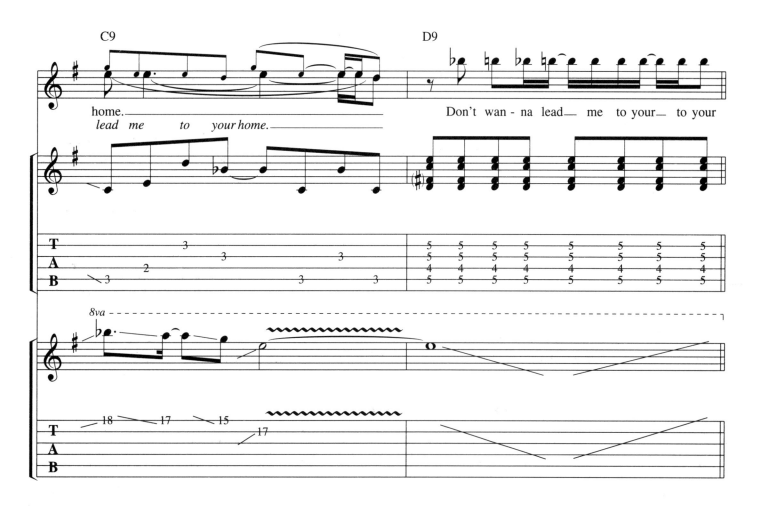

D.S. al Coda

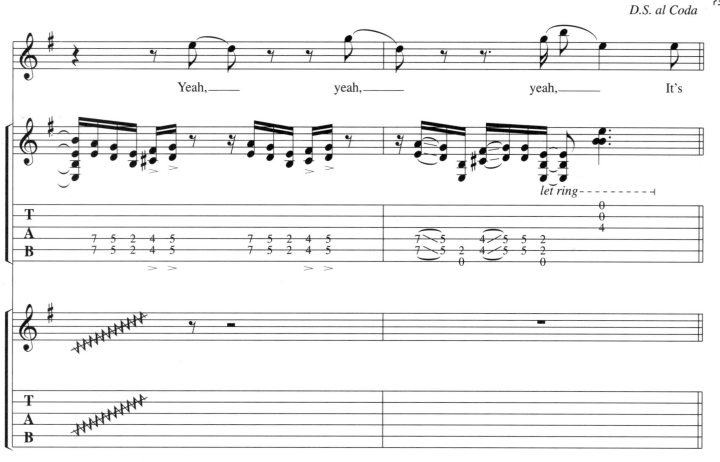

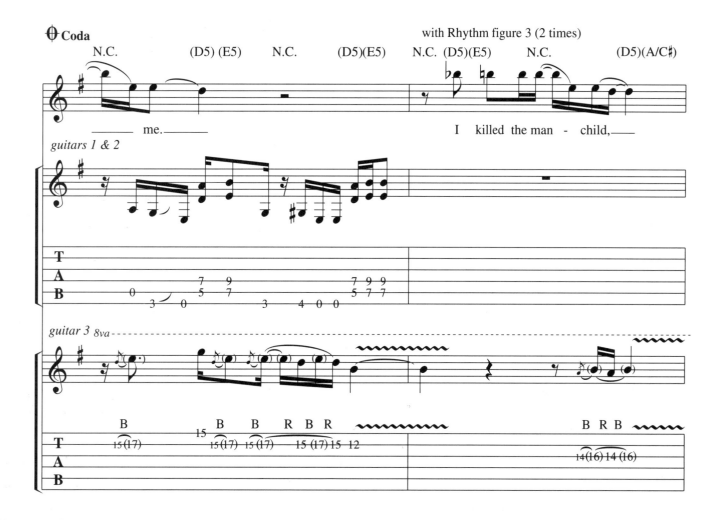

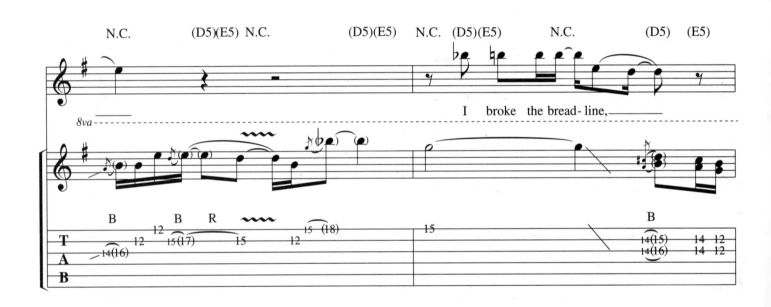

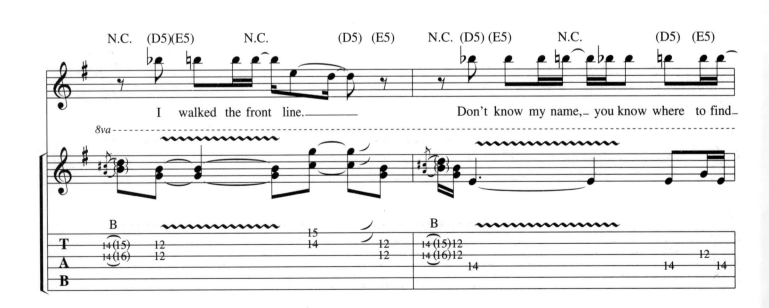

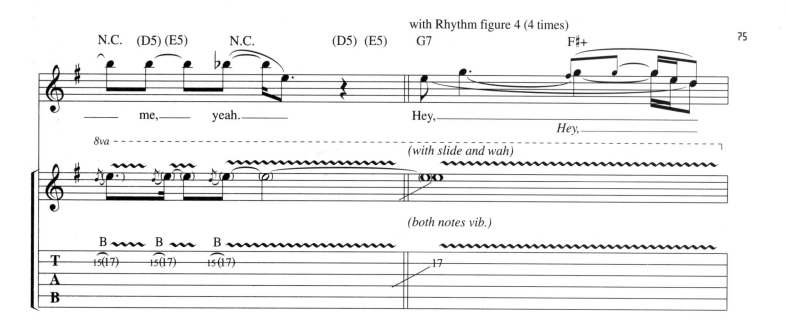

me,_____ yeah._____ Hey,_____

Hey,_____

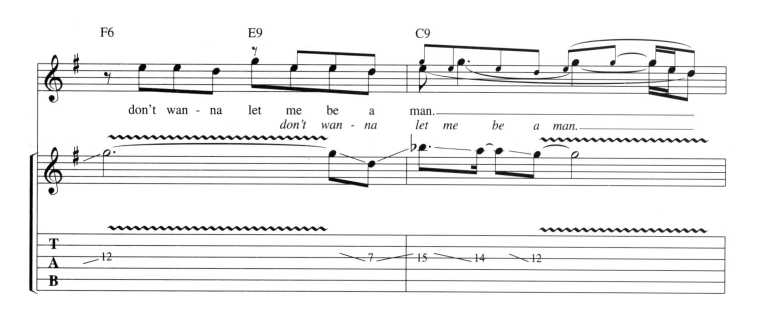

don't wan - na   let   me   be   a   man._____

don't   wan - na   let   me   be   a   man._____

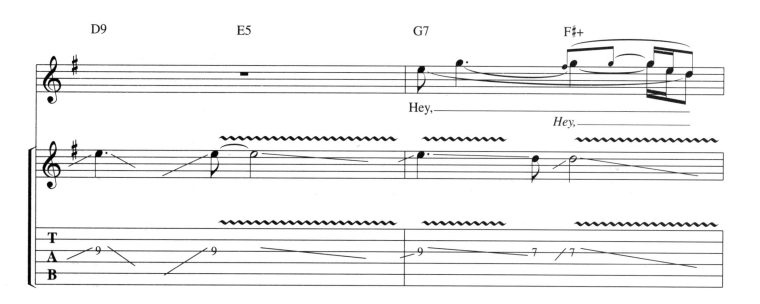

Hey,_____

Hey,_____

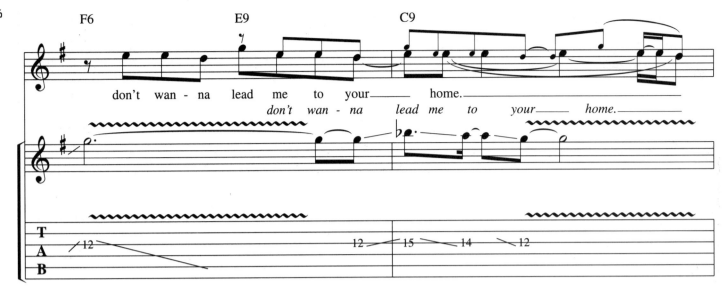

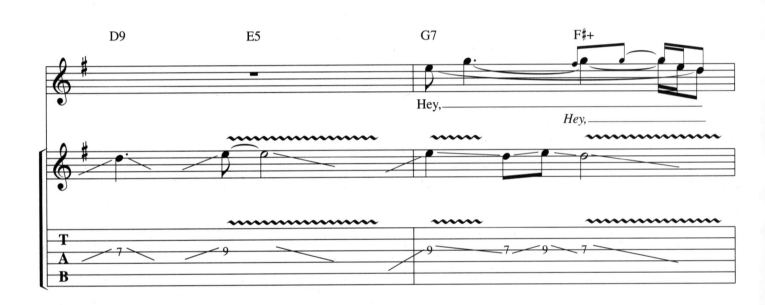

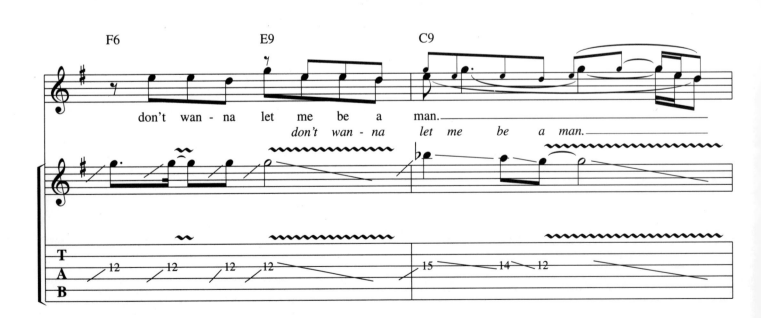

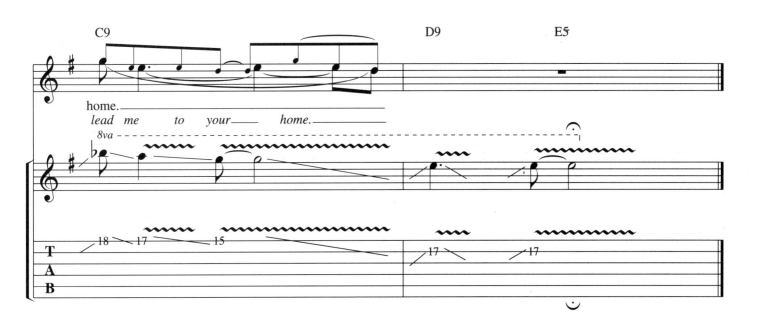

Additional lyrics

2. I killed the manchild, I'll fast alone.
   I had the midwife, naked and alone.
   I mixed the water, I drank the water.
   I killed the brainchild, I'll fast alone.

CRACKERMAN

WORDS AND MUSIC BY SCOTT WEILAND, DEAN DELEO, ROBERT DELEO AND ERIC KRETZ

Moderately fast rock

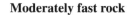

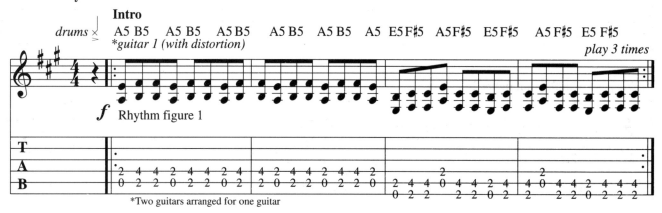

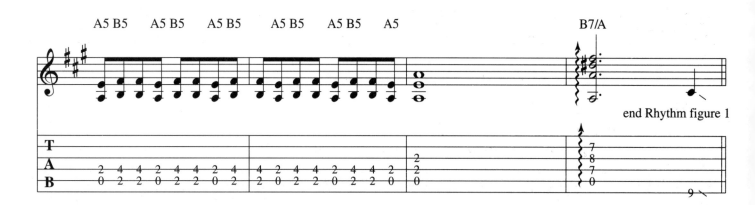

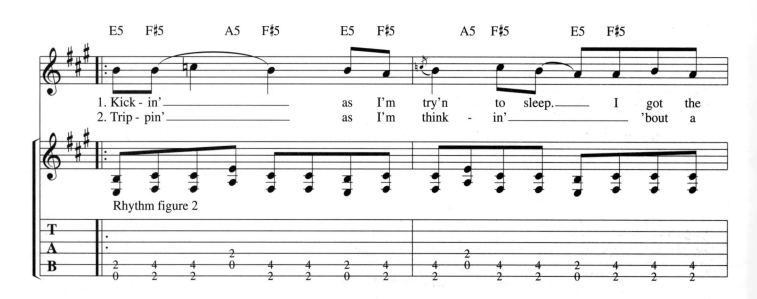

1. Kick - in'_____ as I'm try'n to sleep._____ I got the
2. Trip - pin'_____ as I'm think - in'_____ 'bout a

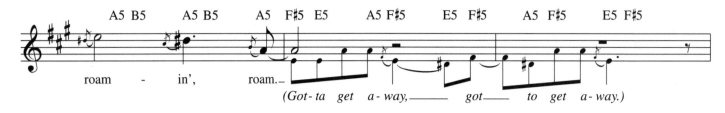

roam - in', roam.___
(Got-ta get a-way,___ got___ to get a-way.)

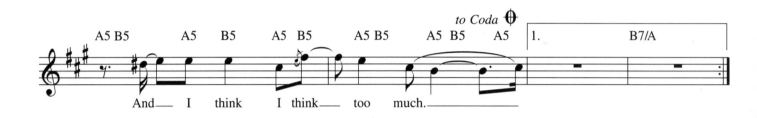

And___ I think I think___ too much.___

Half-time feel

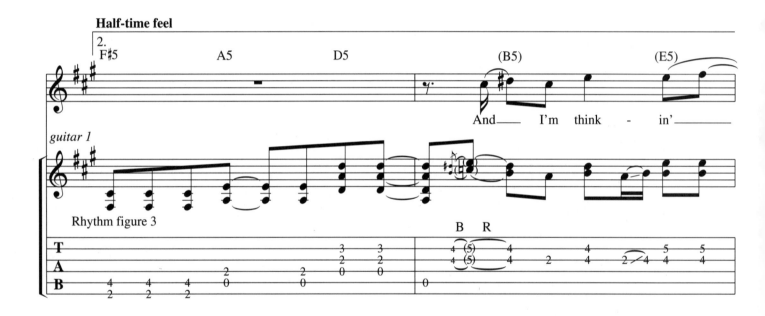

And___ I'm think - in'___

while I'm think - in'.___

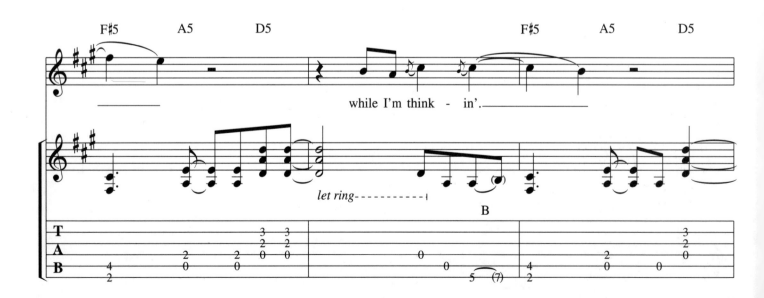

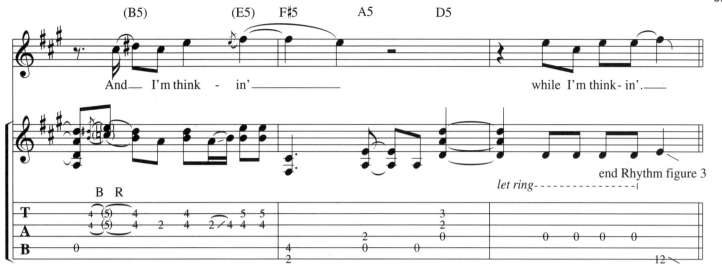

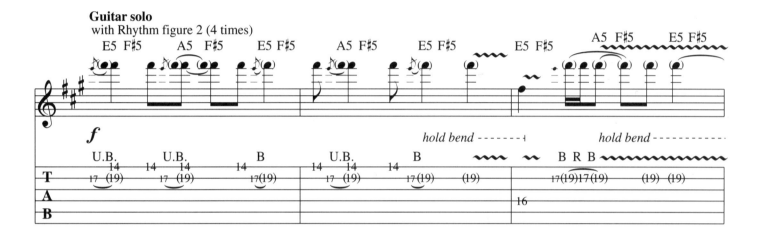

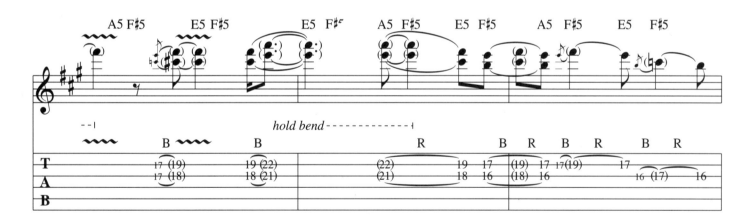

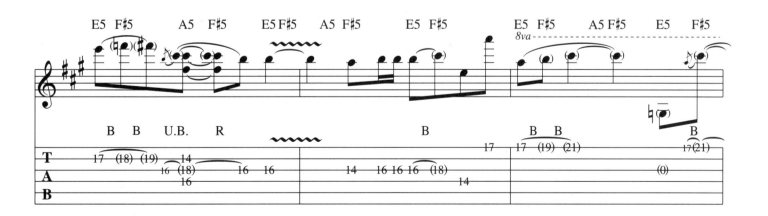

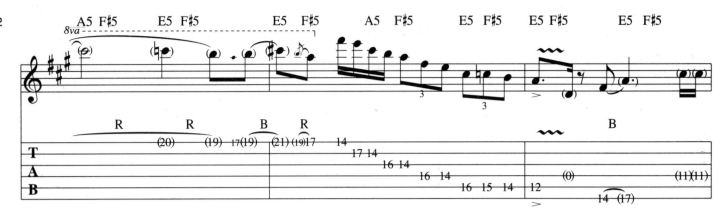

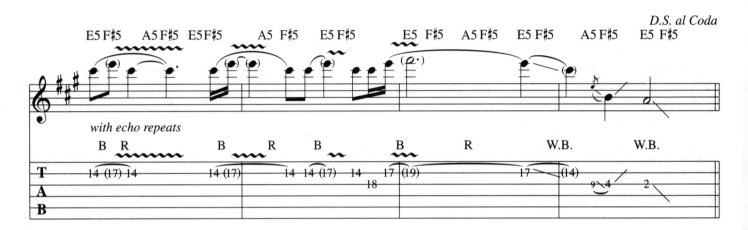

D.S. al Coda

Coda with Rhythm figure 3

Half-time feel

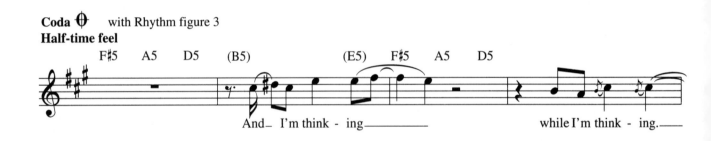

And— I'm think - ing_____ while I'm think - ing.—

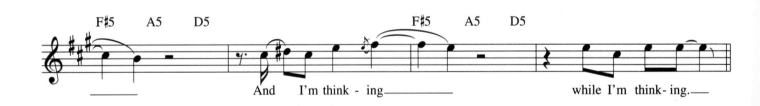

_____ And I'm think - ing_____ while I'm think- ing.—

End half-time feel *with vocal ad lib*

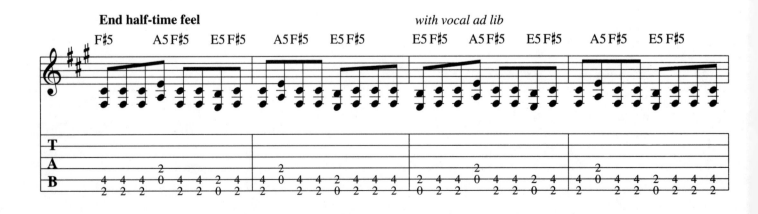

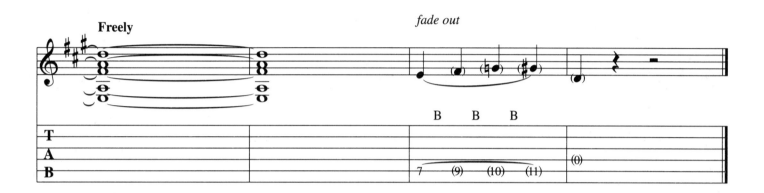

WHERE THE RIVER GOES

WORDS AND MUSIC BY SCOTT WEILAND, DEAN DELEO, ROBERT DELEO AND ERIC KRETZ

Moderate half-time feel
Intro

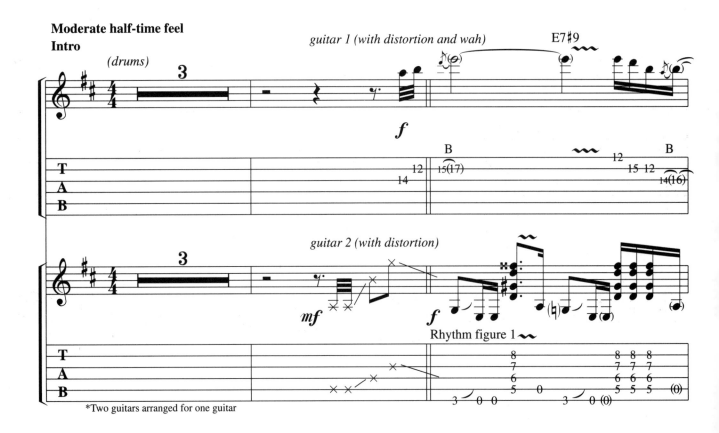

*Two guitars arranged for one guitar

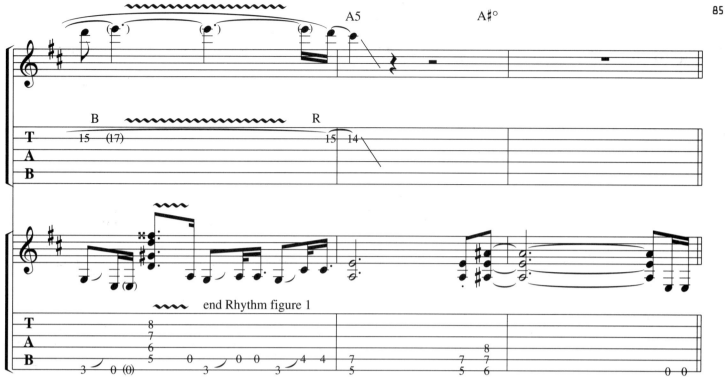

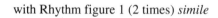

with Rhythm figure 1 (2 times) *simile*

1.,3. *(D.S.)* Yeah,_____ I could hide— in the calm— of the eye—— of a storm— and nev- er blow— a-

way._____

Well,_____ I'm a young - (uh) man— with a knife— to my back,— and

some— things nev- er seem to change._____

end Rhythm figure 2b

with Rhythm figure 1 (2 times) *simile*

E7♯9

2. I_____ wish_ I could live_ in the dream_ that I fly_ on tarred and feath-ered

wings,_____ yeah._ Well,_____ I'm- a los-

ing a game_ of re - al - it- y dice_ where the deal-er nev-er ev- er pays._____

Pre-chorus

with Rhythm figures 2a and 2b *simile*

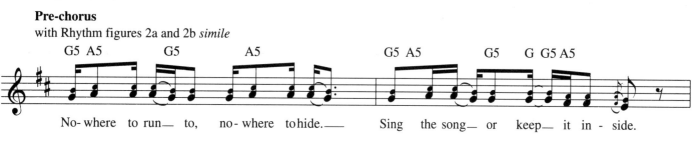

| G5 | A5 | G5 | A5 | G5 | A5 | G5 | G | G5 | A5 |

No- where to run_ to, no- where to hide._ Sing the song_ or keep_ it in - side.

G5 A5   G5   A5   G5 A5   G5 G   G5 G G5 G G5

Bought the farm,_ but the farm- er done died. Sing that song,_ sing that song_ in-

E7♯9   A5   A♯°

side,_____ yeah!_____

Chorus

I wan - na be as big as a moun - tain,— I wan - na fly as high as the sun.—

guitar 2

Rhythm figure 3

palm mute on open D throughout

end Rhythm figure 3

to Coda

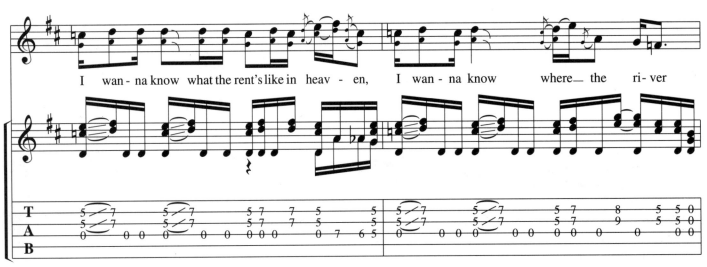

I wan - na know what the rent's like in heav - en, I wan - na know where— the ri - ver

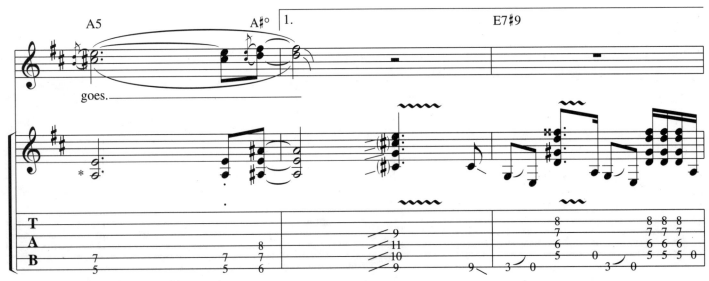

goes.

*Two guitars arranged for one guitar

Bridge

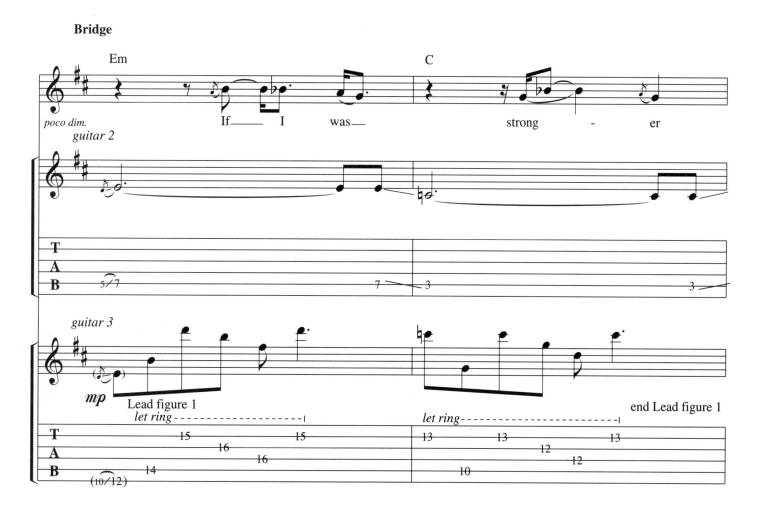

with Lead figure 1 (3 times) *simile*

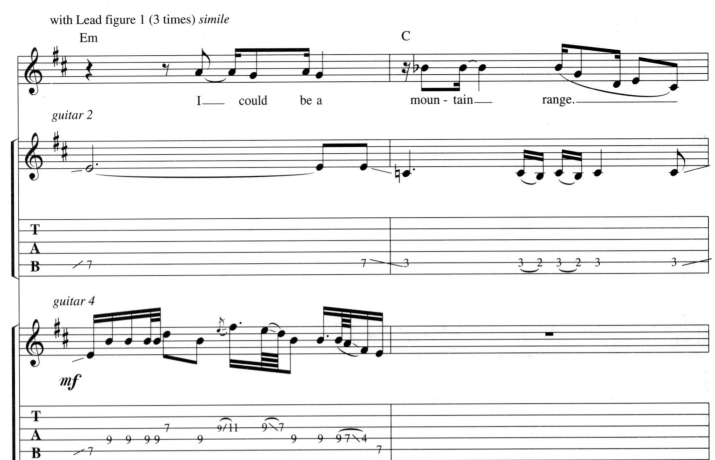

I— could be a moun - tain— range.—

If night— was— long - er,—

Lyrics:
could I es - cape the day?

If I was strong - er I could be a moun - tain range.

If night was long - er, could I es - cape

*Two guitars arranged for one guitar

Guitar solo
with Rhythm figure 1 (2 times) *simile*

guitar 1 (with distortion)

the day?

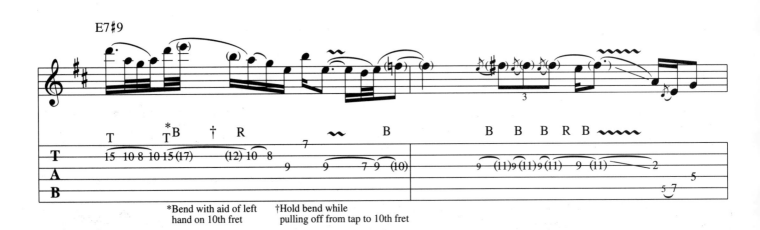

*Bend with aid of left   †Hold bend while
hand on 10th fret   pulling off from tap to 10th fret

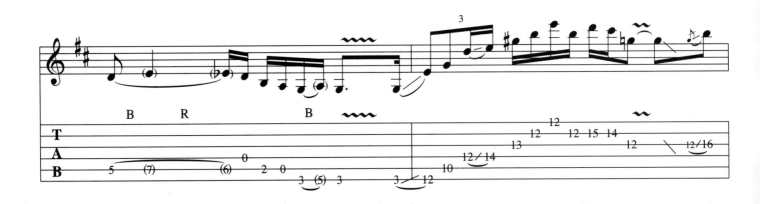

D.S. al Coda

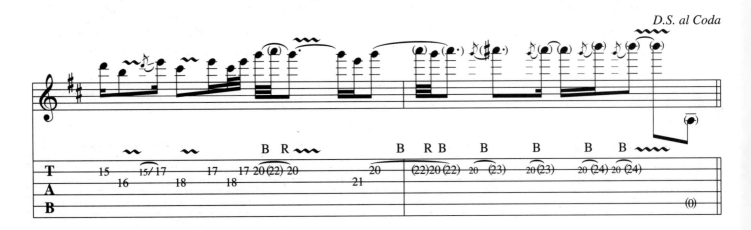

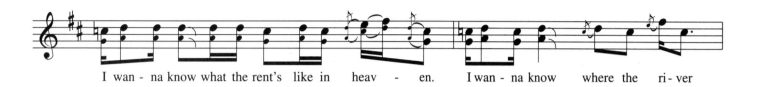

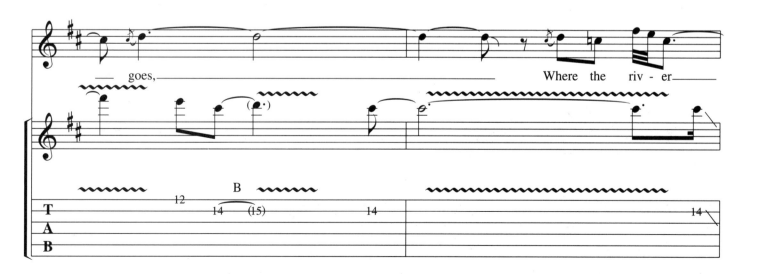

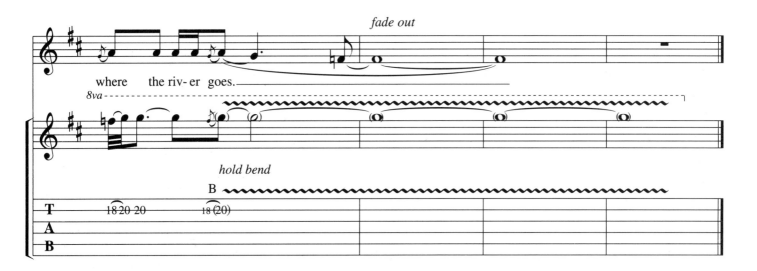

WET MY BED

WORDS AND MUSIC BY SCOTT WEILAND, DEAN DELEO, ROBERT DELEO AND ERIC KRETZ

Moderately

(Background under recitation: play 4 1/2 times)
(Begin recitation 2nd time)

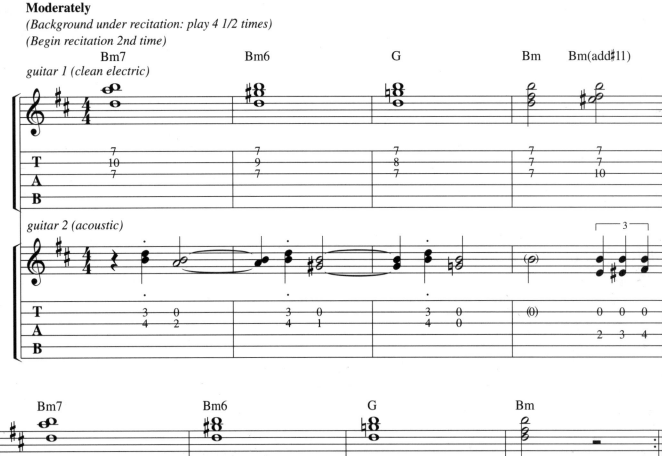

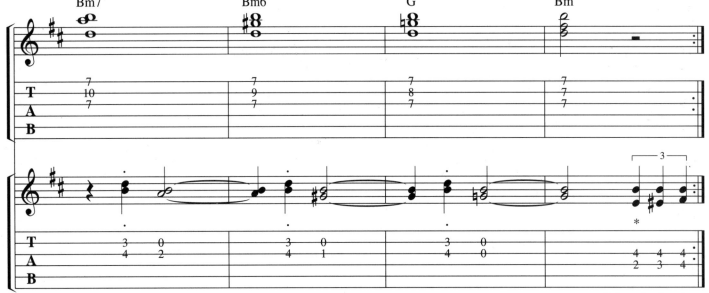

* alternative fingering

Recitation:

Hey everybody, where did Mary go? Where did Mary go?
And where's my only cigarette? Please think for me, I can't bear to…
I'll just lie here for a while, wet myself, wet my bed.
I readied it all for her, you know.
Clean sheets, incense, and lots of fluffy pillows—now soiled.
And where's my cigarette? Did you check the bathroom, the bathtub?
She sleeps there sometimes.
Water cleanses, you know…washes dirt away, makes new.
Maybe she…maybe she…maybe she's…maybe…maybe she swam away.